The Open University

Science: Level 2

S278
EARTH'S PHYSICAL RESOURCES
ORIGIN, USE AND
ENVIRONMENTAL IMPACT

WATER
THE VITAL RESOURCE

SANDY SMITH

The S278 Course Team

Chair

Peter Webb

Course Managers

Annemarie Hedges
Jessica Bartlett

Authors

Tom Argles
Peter Sheldon
Sandy Smith
Peter Webb

Course Assessor

Professor David Manning
(*University of Newcastle*)

Block Assessor

Dr Michael Price

Production Team

Jessica Bartlett (*Indexer*)
Gerry Bearman (*Editor*)
Steve Best (*Graphic artist*)
Kate Bradshaw (*Software designer*)
Roger Courthold (*Graphic artist*)
Rebecca Graham (*Editor*)
Sarah Hack (*Graphic artist*)
Liz Lomas (*Course team assistant*)
Judith Pickering (*Project manager*)
Jane Sheppard (*Graphic designer*)
Andy Sutton (*Software designer*)
Pamela Wardell (*Editor*)
Damion Young (*Software designer*)

Acknowledgements

The S278 Course Team gratefully acknowledges the contributions of members of the S268 *Physical Resources and Environment* Course Team (1995) and of its predecessor, S238 *The Earth's Physical Resources* (1984).

This publication forms part of an Open University course S278 *Earth's Physical Resources: Origin, Use and Environmental Impact*. The complete list of texts which make up this course can be found on the back cover. Details of this and other Open University courses can be obtained from the Student Registration and Enquiry Service, The Open University, PO Box 197, Milton Keynes, MK7 6BJ, United Kingdom: tel. +44 (0)870 333 4340, email general-enquiries@open.ac.uk

Alternatively, you may visit the Open University website at http://www.open.ac.uk where you can learn more about the wide range of courses and packs offered at all levels by The Open University.

To purchase a selection of Open University course materials visit http://www.ouw.co.uk, or contact Open University Worldwide, Michael Young Building, Walton Hall, Milton Keynes MK7 6AA, United Kingdom for a brochure: tel. +44 (0)1908 858785; fax +44 (0)1908 858787; email ouwenq@open.ac.uk

The Open University
Walton Hall, Milton Keynes
MK7 6AA

First published 2005, Second edition 2006.

Edited, designed and typeset by The Open University.

Printed and bound in the United Kingdom at the University Press, Cambridge.

ISBN 0 7492 6996 0

2.1

CONTENTS

WATER USE

1.1 Water as a resource

Water is arguably the most important physical resource studied in this Course as it is the only one that is essential for human survival; we would die very quickly without it. Other physical resources can make life more comfortable, but water makes life possible. If you were shipwrecked on an island, a priority would be to find a source of fresh water fairly quickly; the thought of looking for other physical resources on the island, such as minerals for construction, fuel for warmth or metals for tools would come much later, if at all.

Water is the commonest substance on the Earth's surface. It exists on land, in the oceans and in the atmosphere. Water may be pure or contain dissolved substances, particularly salt, in ocean water, some lakes and deep underground (see Box 1.1). 'Water resources' are usually *fresh* water, with a low content of dissolved, suspended and biological substances. Although water is abundant on Earth, fresh water is much less so, being only a few per cent of the total water, and in some places on Earth it is very scarce.

Water differs from most of the other resources studied in this Course, as it is a *renewable* resource, continuously driven around in a cycle by the energy of the Sun and the Earth's gravity. For example, rain falling on land flows away to the sea in rivers, and so is lost as a fresh water resource. But rain will fall again, replenishing the rivers. The rainfall may be irregular or seasonal, so the renewability of water is not instantaneous but has a delay of a few days or even many years. In comparison with the time needed to form other resources, such as sand and gravel, coal, or petroleum, this time is very short, so water is regarded as a renewable resource.

Problems are caused by the presence of too little water (droughts) or too much water (floods). The 1970s and early 1980s were a time of widespread drought in the Sahel zone of Africa, and in the southern republics of the former USSR, and, on a smaller scale, parts of Britain experienced drought conditions in 1975–76 and 1984, 1989–90, and 1995. Floods were particularly prevalent in 2000, with widespread flooding in Mozambique in Africa, and the UK.

Box 1.1 Properties of water

Water is one of the few substances that commonly exist in each of the three physical states on Earth, as a solid (ice or snow), liquid (water) and a gas (water vapour). What is unusual about water is that its solid form has a lower density than its liquid form, which is rare in other substances. This means that ice floats on water, so water freezes from the top down rather than the other way around. If water froze from the bottom up, then aquatic life would be forced upwards as the water froze, and eventually end up stranded on the surface of the pond, lake, river or sea, instead of being able to survive underneath the ice in liquid water.

Water is an extraordinary solvent; no other liquid dissolves such a large variety of substances, which is why it is ideal for scientists, industrialists and cooks, but unfortunately it means that water can be easily polluted.

Box 1.2   Historical water use

Early humans were hunter–gatherers, roaming from place to place, but their movements were controlled by the need for water. When humans started to grow food, establishing permanent settlements, water was needed for crops and animals as well as for people, so settlements have always grown up near reliable sources of water. Most major towns lie on the banks of rivers, or, where there are no streams or rivers, settlements exist where underground water can be reached by digging wells.

The management of water resources has a long history. The oldest known dam in the world was constructed in Egypt about 5000 years ago, and was used for storing drinking and irrigation water. Farmers in Arabia at this time used the craters of extinct volcanoes as storage tanks for irrigation water and dug deep wells for their drinking water. Excavated ruins in India of similar antiquity retain the remains of water supply and drainage systems, which included baths and swimming pools.

Figure 1.1   Roman aqueduct, Pont-du-Gard, France.

The Romans had sophisticated systems for water supply and sewage disposal in their cities, including great aqueducts to bring clean water from surrounding hills (Figure 1.1).

The amount of water needed for individual survival is very small. The island castaway could live on 1 or 2 litres of drinking water a day if he or she also had a source of food. However, our everyday water requirements are greater than those of the castaway. Even at subsistence level, water is needed for cooking and washing as well as for drinking. The minimum requirement is about 5 litres per person per day, provided there is enough rainfall for growing food. The typical quantity of water used at subsistence level in developing countries is 20–40 litres per person per day. Here people often have no access to safe drinking water; water may be taken directly from a river, pond or well, and used without any form of treatment. However, if water is taken from a well, it is likely to be of good quality because of the purifying properties of the rock through which it has passed.

In high-income, industrialized countries, where a piped water supply is usually available, much more water is used — a typical per capita figure is 500 litres per person per day. Much of this extra demand comes from industry, agriculture and power generation, but part is due to the greater use of water for domestic purposes. The convenience of a piped water supply makes it easy to use water for many purposes other than drinking, cooking and basic washing — for example, washing machines, dishwashers, car washing and flushing WCs (Figure 1.2). Indeed, in some communities, notably the drier regions of the United States, more

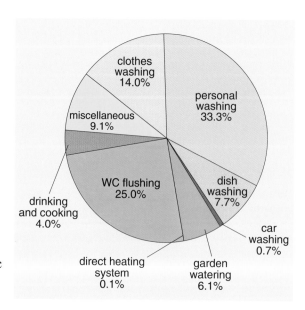

Figure 1.2   The average household water use by category for England and Wales, by purpose, for 1997–8 (Environment Agency, 2001).

than half the domestic water supply is used for watering lawns and flower gardens, a need that would not be thought of in a subsistence-level community. However, on a global scale, only 8% of water use is for domestic purposes (Table 1.1).

Table 1.1   Global water use, 2001.

	Domestic use (%)	Industrial use (%)	Agricultural use (%)
global	8	22	70
high-income countries	11	59	30
low- to middle-income countries	8	10	82

Table 1.2 gives an indication of the quantities of water needed for various domestic purposes, for growing food and for manufacturing.

Table 1.2   Typical water requirements for various domestic purposes, food growing and manufacturing.

Domestic		Manufacturing or industrial		Food growing or agriculture	
Use or product	Quantity of water needed/litres	Use or product	Quantity of water needed/litres	Use or product	Quantity of water needed/litres
WC, per flush	6–10	1 kg (litre) beer	8	1 kg wheat	1000
bath	80–170	1 kg paper	100	1 kg rice	4500
shower, per minute	5–10	1 kg bricks	1–2	1 kg sugar beet	1000
washing machine, per load	up to 80	1 kg steel	5–200	1 kg potatoes	550
dishwasher, per load	25–35	1 kg aluminium	8000		
		1 kg fertilizer	600		
		1 kg refined crude oil	15		
		1 kg synthetic rubber	3000		
		car	380 000		

Note: 1 litre of water weighs 1 kg, and 1 m^3 is 1×10^3 litres and weighs 1 tonne.

Rainfall provides most of the water needed by crops in large areas of the world, but in some areas the rainfall is insufficient or seasonal, and vast quantities of irrigation are needed to grow crops (Box 1.3). On a global scale, more water is used for irrigation than for anything else. Agriculture accounts for 70% of the global water use (Table 1.1), with most used for irrigation.

Industry is the second largest user of water on a global scale, making use of water in many ways. From Table 1.2 you can see that it generally needs much more than a litre (a kilogram) of water to produce a kilogram of product. In addition to the purposes listed in Table 1.2, water is used for building, in the preparation of processed food (such as food-canning), for cleaning, in ore-processing, for waste disposal and for cooling. Electricity generation requires

Box 1.3   Irrigation

Irrigation is used to grow crops in areas where they could otherwise not be grown, or to improve the yield. Around 15% of the world's arable land is irrigated. In arid regions, farming would be impossible without it, as in the deserts of Egypt and Saudi Arabia. Elsewhere, irrigation is used to supplement rainfall and to overcome the high variability of rainfall in semi-arid regions, where rainfall occurs for only a short period during the year and in unpredictable quantities. Irrigation provides security against crop failure and is not confined to arid and semi-arid areas; it is used often, but irregularly, on high-value crops in areas of greater rainfall such as England.

Irrigation is most common in Asia, where it is used particularly for rice-growing in flooded fields. In some parts, rivers are allowed to flood the fields in the rainy season, and rice and other crops are planted as the floods recede. In other places, seasonal rainfall is stored in reservoirs for use in the dry season. Water may also be pumped from underground; this occurs particularly in the south-western USA and the Sahara.

In addition to the flooding of fields, water is fed to crops through channels, by spraying, or by drip feed from holes in pipes (Figure 1.3). The method used varies in cost and efficiency of water use: developing countries usually use channels in the soil, which are cheap but inefficient (much of the water is not used by the crop). Irrigation is especially important for these countries, which may have insufficient rainfall for agriculture and cannot afford to import food. Countries may also use large amounts of water for irrigation to grow high-value crops, such as fruit in the south-western USA (as will be discussed in Box 1.4).

If used inappropriately, irrigation can lead to a major problem — salts present in the irrigation water can accumulate in the soil as the water evaporates, a process called **salinization**. This causes a decline in crop yields until eventually the soil becomes useless for agriculture, but it can be prevented by using enough irrigation water to wash the salts through the soil, and draining this water from the fields.

Figure 1.3   Drip irrigation in Jordan. Hoses are laid out across the fields, with holes at regular intervals in the hoses. Individual plants, in this instance grape vines, are supplied by each hole.

vast quantities of water for cooling. In addition, the energy of falling water is used to turn turbines to generate hydroelectric power.

Water is used in the production of energy, but energy is also needed to supply water: from the human energy needed to carry water from a river or raise it from a well, to the electrical energy needed to pump water around the distribution system to houses and industry. Also part of the energy budget for water resources is the energy used in building dams, digging tunnels, building water treatment plants and so on. Given enough energy, water resources can even be 'created': seawater, for example, can be desalinated to fresh water for an energy cost of about 300 megajoules per cubic metre (300 MJ m^{-3}). (A joule, J, is the SI unit of energy; 1 MJ is 10^6 J.)

Water is also used for transportation, on the sea and on rivers, lakes and canals. Most canals were built for transporting goods, sometimes linking navigable rivers.

They are still important in parts of Europe, but the 3200 km of canals that were built in Britain during the late 18th and early 19th centuries are now little used for their original purpose, as goods can be moved more quickly by rail or road.

Recreational uses of water include angling, sailing and swimming, which can take place in reservoirs as well as in rivers, lakes and the sea. Water also has indirect uses, such as providing salt and fish for food.

The uses of water can be divided into **consumptive uses**, where water is used in such a way as to be temporarily lost as a resource, and **non-consumptive uses** where water is used without major diversions from its natural path and without changing its quality. When water is used in manufacturing industry, for example, this is a consumptive use; the use of water for recreation, such as sailing on a river, is non-consumptive.

Which of the following uses of water would you classify as consumptive, and which as non-consumptive? Domestic water supply; irrigation and other agricultural use; industrial manufacturing; cooling (industrial and electricity generation); hydroelectric power generation; transportation; recreation.

The first four are consumptive uses. Cooling is 'borderline', but in fact about 1% of cooling water is lost by evaporation and the rest is generally returned to the water source at a slightly higher temperature — its quality has changed. It is also diverted from its natural path. The last three are non-consumptive uses.

Where water resources are limited, rapid reuse may be possible. Power stations using cooling towers *recycle* water after cooling, with only a small amount lost through evaporation. Such a cooling system uses less water (about 1/50th) than a power station without cooling towers, which returns warmer water to its source without cooling it. Industry can also reuse water: steel production, for example, can use from 5 to 200 litres of water per kilogram of steel (a difference of 40 times the amount of water), depending on the degree of reuse.

Substitution is possible for some uses of water, but many uses do not have acceptable substitutes.

Question 1.1

Consider the uses of water listed in the question above, and for each use comment on whether a substitute is possible, and what the substitute could be. What do you think is the major disadvantage of using substitutes for water?

1.2   The economics of water

Water has traditionally been regarded as a free resource in the sense that there is nothing to stop anybody collecting their own supply of water from rainfall. Even water from the public supply is very cheap. Although sand and gravel only cost around £12 a tonne in the UK in 2004 (Argles, 2005), the average of £0.80 per tonne (a cubic metre) for supply of mains water in England and Wales is even cheaper. However, some regions of the world are less fortunate. For example, in Kuwait most fresh water is produced by the expensive desalination of seawater, and there the cost of water is far higher.

Because water is generally cheap, it is uneconomic — or at any rate expensive — to transport water in large quantities very far (although it can flow under gravity or be pumped over shorter distances). Water therefore has a high place value (see Sheldon, 2005, for further explanation of place value). There is effectively no world market in water (although there is some trading between nearby countries, for example Turkey transports water to north Cyprus), so what matters is local availability.

We can use concepts of *supply* and *demand* (as reviewed in Sheldon, 2005) to consider the price of water. We need to bear three main points in mind:

1   A certain quantity of water is essential for life — all life, not just human life.

2   In most countries the water supply is under the control of a government organization or nationalized industry, so there is not a free market price for water.

3   The price of water depends on the source of supply; how far it needs to be transported, what treatment is needed, etc.

We can work out the relationship between price and demand for water by first considering the island castaway. For the few litres a day necessary for survival, the castaway would give any price for the water, be it £0.80 or £80 per cubic metre, for without the water he or she would die. This small quantity of water is an essential amount so in this situation the water is *inelastic in demand*; this demand will not change even if the price increases. If the price comes down, water will be put to increasingly more uses, for the subsistence demands of cooking and some washing as well as drinking.

As the demand increases to the quantities used per person in developed countries, the situation becomes more complex, as different uses have different demand–price relationships. Consider domestic use. Only 24% of UK households have water meters (2003). Therefore, many people can use whatever quantity of water they wish and still pay the same flat rate for their water.

In the USA most houses have water meters, and so the cost depends on how much water is used. Small increases in price seem to have little effect on demand but large price increases do reduce demand. The quantity of water used in non-metered houses in the USA is about twice that used in metered houses. After metering in England and Wales, the demand fell by 3–21% in different areas. These findings suggest that the use of meters in domestic consumption leads to *elasticity of demand*. Similar considerations apply to the water used for metered industrial purposes. In recent years several industries have reduced their water bills by redesigning manufacturing processes to use water more efficiently, and electricity generating companies are making increasing use of recycled water for cooling.

The agricultural demand for water is very much influenced by price, so agricultural water is in elastic demand (Box 1.4). A maximum price can be put on the water used for irrigation in terms of the selling price of the crops grown, and this maximum is usually quite low, less than the price that most other users would be able to pay. For example, it takes 1000 litres of water to grow a kilogram of wheat or to produce 5–200 kg of steel (Table 1.2); the steel would fetch a higher price than the wheat, so the steel industry could pay more for its water.

[handwritten margin note: 5–200 ℓ ⇒ 1kg Steel]

Box 1.4 Agricultural water in the south-western USA

The agricultural water supply in the south-western USA provides an illustration of the general principles of supply and demand. The soil and climate are very suitable for agriculture but the rainfall is low, so irrigation is necessary. To meet the demand for irrigation water, local rivers and underground water sources have been used, but these local supplies are insufficient for further agricultural development and water would have to be brought to the area from elsewhere. There is a surplus of water in States to the north of the area, but to transport this water would cost more than the value of the crops grown, so it is not economic to do so. However, if industry rather than agriculture were to expand in the south-western USA, it might become worthwhile to pay the high cost of transporting water to the area. This is a consequence of water economics: water can be supplied to the south-western USA, but only at a high price, and to be economic the water would have to be used for industry rather than agriculture.

The higher the price that water can fetch, the greater the incentive to supply a larger quantity. Small quantities of water might be obtained fairly easily and cheaply from a local river, ignoring, for the moment, the cost of treating the water, and as long as there is water to be abstracted, a small change in price can produce a large change in the amount of water supplied, so the supply is elastic. If the price is higher, wells can be drilled and underground water pumped to the surface. If the price becomes higher still, it becomes economic to pump water from greater depths, or an alternative supply of water may be used (for example, from a distant river or by desalination of seawater).

1.3 Summary of Chapter 1

1   Water is a renewable resource; globally there is a virtually constant supply of fresh water, as water is recycled by natural processes, but it is unevenly distributed.

2   A few litres of water per day are needed per person for human survival. For subsistence, the daily requirement is 20–40 litres per person; this includes the use of water for cooking and washing in addition to drinking, but not water for growing food. Water use in industrialized countries is typically 500 litres per person per day. This includes water for various purposes: domestic, industrial, power generation and agriculture.

3   On a global scale the largest use of water is for agriculture (70%), most of which is for irrigation. 8% of the remaining water is used for domestic purposes, and 22% for industry.

4   The uses of water can be separated into consumptive and non-consumptive. A consumptive use is where water is used in such a way as to be temporarily lost as a resource, as when used for the domestic water supply. In a non-consumptive use, such as transportation, neither the natural route nor the quality of the water is changed.

5   In the UK, water is the cheapest of all physical resources, at an average price of £0.80 per tonne in England and Wales (2004). Supply and demand relationships apply to water as they do to other resources. Water generally has a high place value, as the cost of transporting water would add considerably to its price.

THE WATER CYCLE

2.1   Storage of water in the hydrosphere

The **hydrosphere** includes the parts of the Earth that are mainly water, such as the oceans, ice caps, lakes and rivers. Various parts of the hydrosphere can be seen in Figure 2.1. The oceans are blue; snow and ice are white in the ice caps of the Antarctic, and on high mountains such as Mount Kilimanjaro. (The yellow and brown areas are deserts, and vegetation appears grey-green.)

Water moves over, on and through the Earth in a continuous cycle driven by the Sun and gravity. It is known as the **water cycle** or the **hydrological cycle** (shown by the blue arrows in Figure 2.2) and involves water as liquid, solid (ice and snow) and gas (water vapour). Water can take many different paths through the cycle, but the total volume of water in the water cycle remains virtually constant. There are two main types of water in the cycle:

1   **meteoric water**, which is fresh water derived by condensation from the atmosphere and which accumulates as surface water (rivers and freshwater lakes) and underground water;

2   **saline water**, the seawater of the oceans and many lakes.

Figure 2.1   A view of the Earth from Apollo 17 in 1972. The blue areas are oceans, the white swirls are clouds and the uniformly white area is the Antarctic ice cap.

Small amounts of magmatic water from the interior of the Earth are *added* to the cycle by volcanic eruptions. On the other hand, water trapped within the pores of sediment, formation water, is, at least in the short term, *isolated* from the water cycle. This can either be water that was originally trapped in the sediments during their formation, or water that percolated into the rocks later. Formation water is usually saline, mainly because most sediments are marine and the water trapped in the sediments would be seawater.

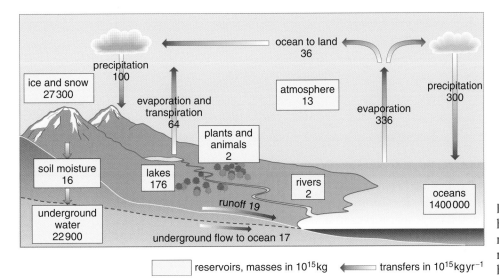

Figure 2.2   The water, or hydrological, cycle. Water moves (blue arrows) between reservoirs (boxes) of the hydrosphere.

All parts of the hydrosphere store water temporarily, and are called **reservoirs**. These natural reservoirs of the hydrosphere are not to be confused with the human-built reservoirs used to store water on land: for example, the atmosphere is a reservoir, containing 13×10^{15} kg of water. The study of water movement upon and beneath the ground and the physics and chemistry of the water is called **hydrology**.

● What are the main ways in which water is transferred between the various reservoirs of the hydrosphere shown in Figure 2.2?

○ Evaporation and transpiration, precipitation, runoff from land and underground flow of water to the ocean.

Water resides for different lengths of time in different reservoirs. The average length of time that water stays in a reservoir before moving to another is called the **residence time** for that reservoir (Table 2.1). A hydrosphere reservoir empties and replenishes at the same rate, and the residence time is calculated from the rate of replenishment in relation to the volume of the reservoir. There may be several ways in which water is transferred to and from a reservoir (Figure 2.2).

$$\text{residence time} = \frac{\text{mass in reservoir}}{\text{rate of transfer from or to reservoir}} \qquad (2.1)$$

For example, the residence time for rivers, assuming the only significant transfer from rivers is by runoff:

$$\text{river residence time} = \frac{2 \times 10^{15}\ \text{kg}}{19 \times 10^{15}\ \text{kg yr}^{-1}}$$

$$= 0.11 \text{ years (about 5 weeks)}$$

Table 2.1 Residence times for water in the water cycle.

Reservoir	Percentage of total water	Residence time
ocean	95.9	about 4000 years
ice caps	3.0	about 800 years
underground water	1.0	a few weeks to more than 10 000 years
lakes	0.025	a few years
soil moisture	0.005	a few weeks to 1 year
atmosphere	0.001	about 11 days
rivers	0.000 07	a few weeks

Residence time is a concept that can be applied to any cyclical process, not just the water cycle. Figure 2.2 shows that the transfers of the cycle are in balance: in particular, water lost to the atmosphere by evaporation and transpiration is balanced by water returned by precipitation. The residence time gives an indication of how quickly water in a hydrosphere reservoir can be renewed. The shortest residence time, 11 days, is for water vapour in the atmosphere, which is continually renewed by evaporation from the oceans and the land, and is lost by precipitation. This is a rapid *subcycle* of the water cycle. Subcycles involving the oceans, the ice caps and underground water are much slower (Table 2.1).

There is a large volume of fresh water locked up in the polar ice caps (Table 2.1), but these are far from the centres of population and the arid countries that need it. It is not economic to transport this water at the moment, but it may become so in the future (Section 6.1).

Figure 2.3 The Dead Sea, in the Middle East. This lake contains large quantities of water, but is even more saline than seawater, so it is not practical to use it as a water resource.

Apart from the oceans and ice caps, the greatest volume of water is underground, stored in porous rocks below the Earth's surface. The shallower underground water moves quite quickly through the cycle and is fresh water, so it can be used for water resources. But it is only a small proportion of the total underground water, and its residence time is relatively short, ranging from a few weeks to a few years. Underground water below a depth of a few hundred metres moves more slowly through the cycle, and residence times are much longer, up to ten thousand years (Table 2.1). Much of this water is saline either because it has had time to dissolve salts from the rocks, or because it originates from seawater.

The world's lakes contain large volumes of water (Table 2.1) and are more accessible than the polar ice caps. However, over half of these lakes are saline (Figure 2.3), and 80% of the water in the freshwater lakes occurs in only 40 large lakes, including the Great Lakes of North America (32×10^{15} kg) and Lake Baikal in Asia (22×10^{15} kg). Rivers are very useful for water resources. Although they store very little water (Table 2.1), the water in them is rapidly renewed — it has a residence time of just a few weeks.

The water found underground and in the ice caps, lakes and rivers forms about 4% of the total in the water cycle; but because the deeper underground water, the ice caps and the saline lakes are not usable as sources of water at the moment, the amount of water that can be used for water resources is much less, only about 1% of the total. This water is distributed very unevenly, as can be appreciated when we hear about the extensive water shortages and droughts in many parts of the world. In order to understand the problems of availability and distribution of water in more detail, we shall now look at the processes in the water cycle that transfer water between the reservoirs of the hydrosphere.

2.2 Precipitation

Water that transfers from the atmosphere to the Earth's surface is called **precipitation**. It may be in the form of rain, snow or hail. Water vapour may also precipitate by condensing as dew or hoar frost. Water in the atmosphere, although one of the smallest reservoirs, is the most important reservoir of water. It exists as vapour, liquid (clouds and raindrops) or in solid form (snow and ice). When air rises (as it does when it moves over mountains), it expands, owing to the decrease in pressure with altitude, and as it expands it cools at a rate of

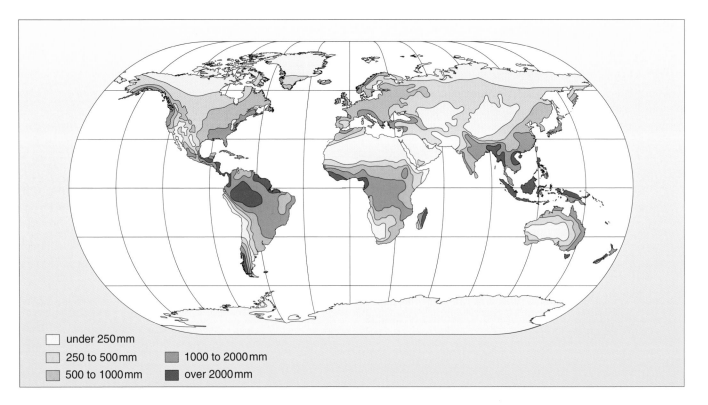

under 250 mm
250 to 500 mm
500 to 1000 mm
1000 to 2000 mm
over 2000 mm

around 1 °C per 100 metres of altitude. As the air cools, water vapour condenses around small particles suspended in the air, such as pollen grains, fungal spores, dust and salt from sea spray. This condensation results in the formation of clouds composed of 0.001–0.1 mm diameter droplets. Precipitation of this water occurs when these droplets coalesce to form larger drops about 1 mm in diameter, or when ice crystals form and they fall to the Earth's surface.

The net effect of the water cycle is to transfer some 36×10^{15} kg of fresh water each year from the oceans to the land by precipitation (Figure 2.2). Globally, precipitation is distributed very unevenly — both geographically and seasonally. Figure 2.4 shows the global distribution of precipitation on land. Some areas get less than 250 mm annually (precipitation is usually measured in millimetres); these are usually deserts, such as in North Africa, the Middle East, central Asia and central Australia. Some of these are visible as the yellow/buff areas in Figure 2.1. The annual rainfall in other areas may reach as much as 12 000 mm; this heavy rainfall is characteristic of the Amazon Basin and parts of South and South-East Asia. The greatest recorded rainfall in 24 hours was 1870 mm on Reunion Island, Indian Ocean, in 1952.

Precipitation can vary in amount from year to year, and in many regions it is seasonal, as on the Indian subcontinent where the south-west monsoon brings rain for a few months in the summer only. Irregular rainfall is common in drier areas, where rain may fall for only a few days each year; the equivalent of a year's rain may fall in one storm lasting a few hours.

The yearly irregularity of rainfall in some areas can be seen in Figure 2.5, which gives the precipitation in Niamey, the capital of Niger, in sub-Saharan Africa (the Sahel). Areas such as the Sahel, with a fairly low rainfall and high variability, are

Figure 2.4 Average annual precipitation on land areas.

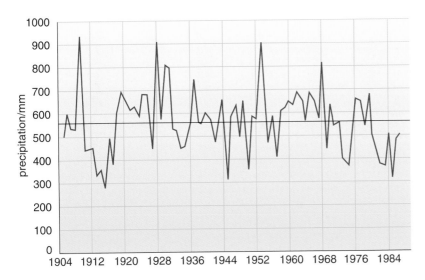

Figure 2.5 Annual precipitation values for Niamey, in Niger, for 1905–87. The horizontal line is the mean annual precipitation, which is 562 mm.

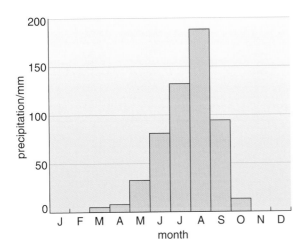

Figure 2.6 Mean monthly precipitation values for Niamey. Precipitation occurs in the months of March to October only.

classed as semi-arid, and are vulnerable to drought in years of lower than average rainfall. Another feature of the precipitation in the Sahel is the seasonality of the rain — Niamey averages only 44 rainy days a year, confined to a rainy season (Figure 2.6).

Question 2.1

(a) What is the range (minimum and maximum) of annual precipitation for Niamey in 1905–87?

(b) What is the minimum annual precipitation as a percentage of the mean annual precipitation for Niamey?

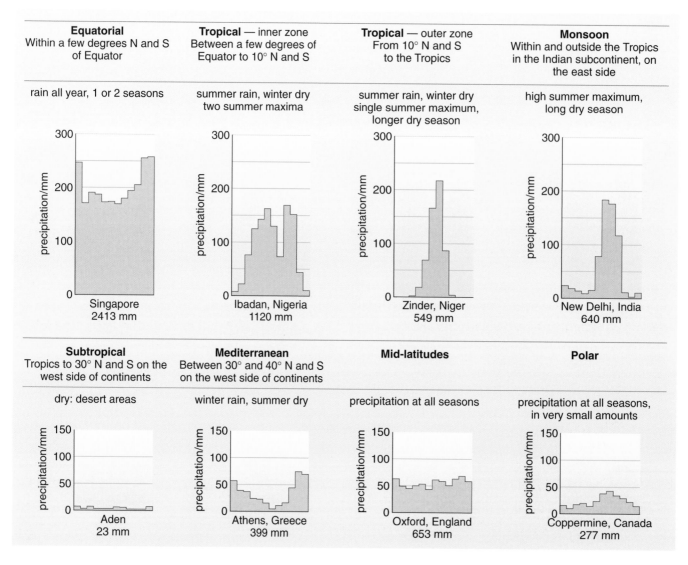

Figure 2.7 Global precipitation regimes.

Niamey is in a different global precipitation regime to the UK (Figure 2.7). Each regime has a characteristic annual precipitation and seasonal pattern.

Because of the prevailing westerly winds (due to its position in mid-latitudes), the UK's precipitation is more evenly distributed throughout the year (Figures 2.7 and 2.8) and more constant from year to year than in many other countries. The amount of precipitation does, however, vary from place to place (Figures 2.8 and 2.9). In the east of England the average annual precipitation is about 500 mm, but in mountainous parts of north-west Scotland, the Lake District and North Wales it can reach over 3200 mm (Figure 2.9).

Question 2.2

(a) What is the range of mean monthly precipitation for each part of the UK in Figure 2.8?

(b) Which UK country has the lowest range of mean monthly precipitation and which two have the highest ranges?

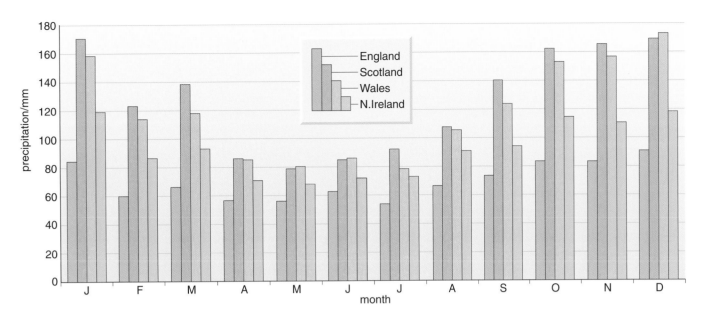

Figure 2.8   Mean monthly precipitation values for England, Scotland, Wales and Northern Ireland, for 1971–2000.

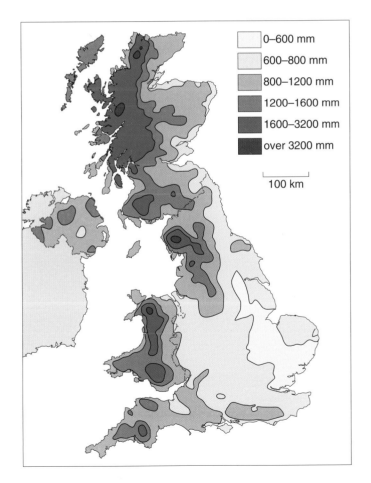

Figure 2.9   The mean annual precipitation in the UK, 1971–2000.

Why is there such a difference in precipitation in different parts of the UK? Precipitation over the UK is the result of one or more of three basic reasons:

- *Altitude* Precipitation increases with altitude over upland areas. When air rises, it cools, causing precipitation, and this occurs when the prevailing westerly airstreams are deflected upward over coastal mountains in Scotland, the Lake District and Wales, the wettest parts of mainland UK.

- *Low-pressure weather systems* Bands of rain are associated with the passage of warm and cold fronts mainly west to east across the UK.

- *Heating of the ground surface* Heating of the ground surface causes convective heating of the atmosphere, giving local showers and thunderstorms.

The regional variation is caused by differences in altitude and in the paths of low-pressure weather systems crossing the UK. More weather systems pass across the north of the UK than the south, so the north is wetter. This creates an uneven distribution of precipitation in Britain, especially in relation to population density: the sparsely inhabited mountainous areas, with the lowest demands for water, have the highest precipitation (see Chapter 7).

2.3 Interception, evaporation and transpiration

Most precipitation reaches the ground, but not all of it, as some is stopped by vegetation, a process known as **interception**. This is part of a subcycle of the water cycle, involving precipitation, interception and evaporation back to the atmosphere, bypassing that part of the main cycle where water reaches the ground. **Evaporation** is the process by which water is transferred as vapour from the land or ocean to the atmosphere.

The proportion of the precipitation that does not reach the ground, the **interception loss**, depends on the type of vegetation, its age, density of planting and the season of the year. The interception loss is 15–35% for coniferous forests and 9–25% for broad-leaved forests (values averaged over a year; the lower values are for tropical rainforest and the higher values for temperate forests). For grassland interception loss is usually lower than for forest, 14–19% for natural grasses. Crops have highly variable values — about 7% for oats, 16% for corn and about 40% for clover, for example. In arid and semi-arid areas, where there is little vegetation, the interception loss is negligible.

The rate of evaporation increases with temperature. The process also depends on the **humidity** (a measure of how close the air is to saturation with water vapour) and the wind speed. The greater the humidity, the less the evaporation. Wind carries moist air away from the ground surface, so wind decreases the local humidity and allows more water to evaporate. The rate of evaporation is highest from open water. Over the ground surface the rate of evaporation depends on the type of soil and the extent to which the ground is saturated with water. Evaporation from a saturated sandy soil can take place nearly as quickly as it can from open water, whereas evaporation from a saturated clay soil is slower, between 75% and 90% of the rate from open water.

Figure 2.10 shows how evaporation and precipitation vary with latitude. Over two-thirds of total global evaporation occurs within 30° of the Equator, because of the higher temperatures in equatorial and tropical areas. Evaporation reaches its greatest values not at the Equator itself, but between latitudes of 10° and 20° in both hemispheres. The strong trade winds at these latitudes carry water vapour towards the Equator, giving very high precipitation in the equatorial zone where the trade-wind systems converge.

Evaporation also varies with season, because of its dependence on temperature and humidity. In the UK, for example, evaporation is low in winter and high in summer (Figure 2.11). So although precipitation averaged over England is not very seasonal (it is more so in Scotland and Wales; Figure 2.8), the *availability of water* is due in large part to the seasonality of evaporation.

Question 2.3

Figure 2.10 shows that evaporation from the Earth's surface is greater in the Southern Hemisphere than in the Northern Hemisphere. Suggest an explanation for this.

Vegetation increases the amount of water returned to the air — not only by interception and then evaporation, but also by **transpiration**. This is the process by which plants draw up water from the soil and transfer it to their leaves, from which it evaporates through pores in the leaf system. Transpiration is controlled essentially by the factors that affect evaporation, and by the type of plant. A considerable amount of water can be transferred to the atmosphere by transpiration: for example, a cabbage transpires about 25 litres of water in total during its growth to full size, and a large oak tree transpires about 400 litres of water each day when in leaf.

Evaporation and transpiration are parts of the hydrological cycle that are difficult to quantify, as it is hard to measure the transfer to water vapour directly. Over land areas it is also difficult to separate the effects of evaporation and transpiration, so the two are usually combined into one parameter, called **evapotranspiration**. Although actual evapotranspiration is difficult to measure, it is relatively easy to calculate a *maximum* value of evaporation for a saturated surface, such as open water, using local meteorological parameters such as humidity, temperature and wind speed. This is called the **potential evapotranspiration** for a particular area. It is the maximum possible evapotranspiration that could take place given an unlimited supply of moisture. Because most land surfaces are neither open water nor saturated, and are partly or wholly covered in vegetation, actual values of evapotranspiration are always less than potential evapotranspiration.

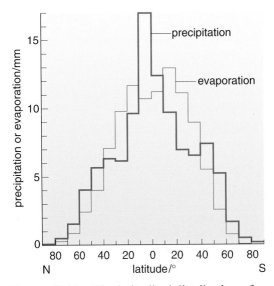

Figure 2.10   The latitudinal distribution of annual precipitation and annual evaporation, expressed in terms of the percentage of the total global precipitation or evaporation within each ten-degree latitude belt.

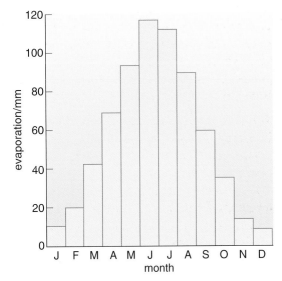

Figure 2.11   Average monthly evaporation for Kempton Park reservoir, in the Thames valley, 1956–62.

In Britain, values of annual potential evapotranspiration increase from a minimum of 355 mm in the north to a maximum of 560 mm in the south (Figure 2.12).

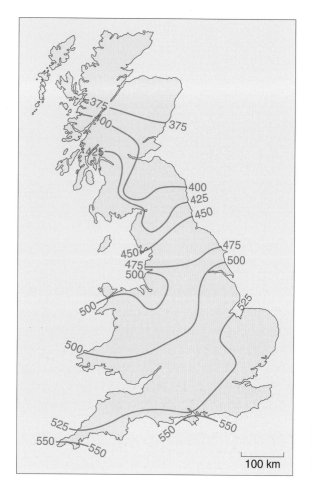

Figure 2.12   Annual potential evapotranspiration in Britain. The red lines are the evapotranspiration contoured values, in mm.

○   Are the areas of greatest precipitation in Britain also the areas of greatest potential evapotranspiration?

○   No. The areas of greatest precipitation in Britain are north-west of Scotland, the Lake District and North Wales (Figure 2.9), whereas the greatest potential evapotranspiration is in the South.

○   Is the potential evapotranspiration in Britain greater or less than the precipitation?

○   In Britain and other places with a temperate climate, the potential (and actual) evapotranspiration is usually less than the precipitation. The exception is in parts of the east of England where the values of potential evapotranspiration and precipitation are similar (Figures 2.9 and 2.12). However, this is true only on an annual basis, as evapotranspiration is much higher in summer than in winter.

Evapotranspiration is usually greater than precipitation in the summer months, and less than precipitation in winter (Figure 2.13). There are also many areas of the world where the potential evapotranspiration is much greater than the precipitation — usually hot areas where precipitation is low (Figure 2.4). In parts of North Africa and the Middle East the precipitation may be less than 50 mm a year, but the potential evapotranspiration is about 3000 mm a year (Figure 2.14). However, the actual evapotranspiration in these areas is much less than potential evapotranspiration because there is usually little water to be evaporated.

The precipitation that is not intercepted, evaporated or transpired back to the atmosphere either soaks into the ground or becomes surface flow. A rough indication of the quantity of water available from underground or from rivers in any area is given by the excess of precipitation over actual evapotranspiration. This is called the **hydrologically effective precipitation**. Underground water and surface water are examined in more detail in Chapters 3 and 4.

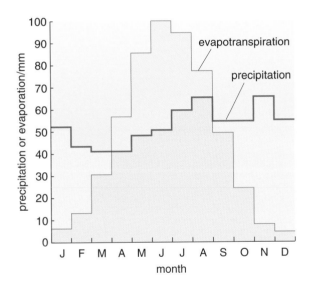

Figure 2.13 Precipitation (thick blue line) and potential evapotranspiration (thin red line) in the Anglian water company region. The blue shading represents the excess of precipitation over potential evapotranspiration in the winter months and the red shading represents a greater potential evapotranspiration than precipitation in the summer months.

Figure 2.14 The Eastern desert in Jordan. This area has about 50 mm of precipitation a year and a potential evapotranspiration of up to 3000 mm a year. Crops cannot be grown in this arid area, and natural vegetation is very sparse.

2.4 Summary of Chapter 2

1   The water cycle involves the movement of water, in all its forms, over, on and through the rocks near the surface of the Earth in a cycle. This cycle is driven by the Sun's energy and the Earth's gravity. The total volume of water in the cycle is virtually constant. Magmatic water adds small amounts of water to the cycle, and formation water removes small amounts of water from the cycle. Water is stored in the natural reservoirs of the hydrosphere: in the oceans, underground, in the ice caps, and in lakes, rivers, the soil and the atmosphere. There is a transfer of water to the oceans from the land surface by rivers and by outflow of underground water.

2   The residence time for water in a reservoir is the average length of time that water remains in that reservoir. It is calculated by dividing the mass in a particular reservoir by the rate of transfer to or from the reservoir. Residence time is a measure of the rate at which water in different parts of the cycle is renewed: it is fastest in the atmosphere (about 11 days) and rivers (a few weeks). Only about 4% of the water in the water cycle is not seawater. The proportion of fresh water which can be used for water supplies is less than this, about 1% of the total.

3   Precipitation has a very uneven global distribution, but is greatest near the Equator. On a smaller scale, precipitation is greatest over mountainous areas on land. Interception is the process by which precipitation is prevented from reaching the ground by vegetation.

4   Water is returned to the atmosphere by evaporation and transpiration. Transpiration is the process by which plants draw water from the soil, transfer it to their leaves and it then evaporates. Evaporation and transpiration can be combined into one parameter, evapotranspiration. A maximum theoretical value for evapotranspiration, called potential evapotranspiration, can be calculated from meteorological parameters for any area.

GROUNDWATER

3.1 Water underground

Many people have the impression that underground water occupies vast caverns, such as those in the Derbyshire Peak District, flowing from one cavern to another along underground rivers. This is a common misconception: underground caverns are fairly rare, but huge quantities of water exist underground, *within* rocks. This is because many rocks contain **pores**, spaces that come in all shapes and sizes. In sediments, and consequently sedimentary rocks, there are often pores between grains (Figure 3.1) which can be filled with water. There may also be spaces between rock beds or along joints, fractures or fissures (Figure 3.2) which can also contain water. However, before we look at pores in more detail we will examine how water gets into the rock.

Figure 3.1 An electron microscope photograph of a sandstone. Pores make up about 30% of the rock's volume. The largest grains are about 0.3 mm long.

Figure 3.2 Bedding planes, joints, fractures and fissures in a limestone cliff face. Such features may enable water to accumulate in rock strata.

3.2 Infiltration

Precipitation that reaches the ground either runs off at the surface, or sinks into it. **Infiltration** is the movement of water through the ground surface into the soil and on downwards. The rate at which infiltration can take place depends, among other things, on the **permeability** of the soil or rock. Permeability is a measure of the ease with which water can move through a substance: the greater the permeability, the easier the infiltration. We shall deal with permeability of rocks more fully in Section 3.6. The total amount of infiltration also depends on the time available for water to seep into the ground. Heavy rainfall usually results in rapid runoff, and relatively little infiltration into the ground.

Question 3.1

To what extent will each of (a) dense vegetation, (b) steeply sloping land, (c) roads and buildings, and (d) frozen subsoil, have an effect on the total amount of infiltration, and why?

There are two distinct zones containing water beneath the ground surface (Figure 3.3). The **unsaturated zone** has mainly air-filled pores, with water held by surface tension in a film around the soil or rock particles. Water moves downwards by gravity through this zone, into the **saturated zone** beneath, in which all the pores are filled with water. The boundary surface between the unsaturated zone and the saturated zone is the **water table**, which is the level of water in a well (strictly, in a well that just penetrates to the water table). Water below the water table, in the saturated zone, is **groundwater**. Just above the water table is a zone called the capillary fringe, in which water has not yet reached the water table, because it has been held up by **capillary retention**. In this process water tends to cling to the walls of narrow openings. The width of the capillary fringe depends on the size of the pore spaces and the number of interconnected pores. It is generally greater for small pore spaces than for larger ones.

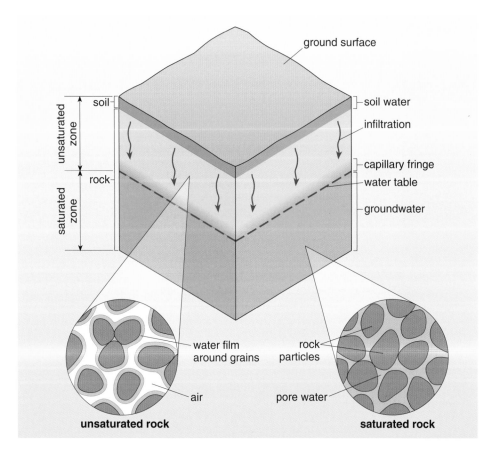

Figure 3.3 Underground water: the infiltration process, the unsaturated zone, the saturated zone and groundwater.

The thickness of the unsaturated zone depends mainly on the climate (particularly the precipitation), but also on the topography (Section 3.3). In arid and mountainous regions this zone may be hundreds of metres thick, whereas in areas of high rainfall it may be only a few metres thick. Beneath swamps, lakes or rivers, the saturated zone reaches to the surface. The thickness of the capillary zone will depend on the soil or rock texture, from a few millimetres in gravel to several metres in chalk or clay, and sometimes this zone may reach the surface. The saturated zone extends downwards as far as the permeability of the rock will allow – a few tens of metres in some places, a kilometre or more in others. Water movement in the saturated zone is predominantly *sideways* (unlike in the unsaturated zone, where it is mainly *downwards*).

3.3 The water table

The water table is a fundamental reference surface in the study of groundwater. It tends to follow the ground surface, rising under hills and falling at valleys, but the gradient of the water table is usually much less than that of the ground surface (Figure 3.4). Under hills the water table is usually at greater depths below the surface than it is below valleys. Where the rocks are very permeable, water can flow through them easily, so the water table will be flatter. Where the water table intersects the ground surface (Figure 3.4c), groundwater will flow out as springs, or directly to streams or rivers.

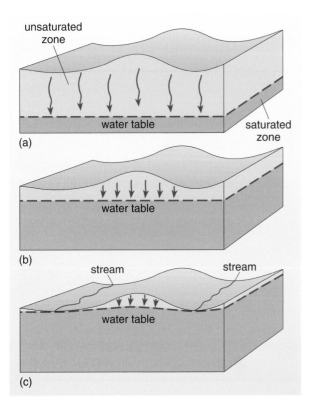

Figure 3.4 The water table. As water sinks into the ground and accumulates (a), the water table rises as a horizontal plane in (b) until it reaches the ground surface in the valleys in (c), where groundwater seeps out as springs and to streams on the surface; with continued infiltration, the water table is no longer horizontal or planar.

The water table can be mapped from the elevation (i.e. the height above ordnance datum, which is roughly sea level) of the water in wells. Figure 3.5a is a map of an outcrop of Triassic sandstones in part of Nottinghamshire, showing both the ground surface and water table contours. Figure 3.5b is a N–S cross-section across the area in Figure 3.5a.

Question 3.2

Answer the following questions, using Figure 3.5.

(a) Is the water table nearer to the surface of the ground in the northern or southern part of the area?

(b) What is the general direction of the slope of the water table?

(c) What is the relationship between undulations in the water table and the topography?

(d) At what depth below the surface of the ground will the water table be found on the highest ground in the figure (i.e. at about 5 km south of Worksop)?

The general slope of the water table in Figure 3.5 is in the same direction as the slope of the ground surface, and undulations of the water table follow undulations of the ground. The water table does not, however, slope as steeply as the ground surface.

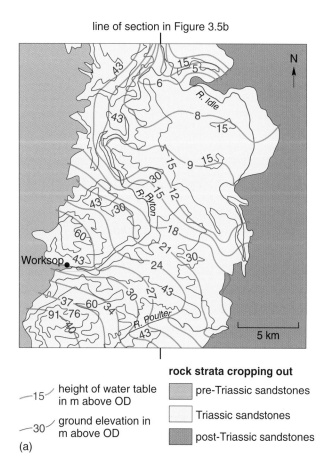

(a)

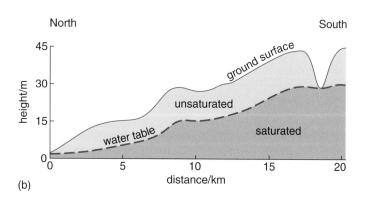

(b)

Figure 3.5 (a) Geological and water table map for the Triassic sandstones in part of Nottinghamshire. The topographic ground surface contours are shown in brown and the water table contours in blue. Higher areas of the ground surface and areas where the water table rises have higher contour values. Water table contours are given in metres above ordnance datum (OD).
(b) N–S cross-section of the outcrop through the Triassic sandstones along the line shown in (a). The vertical scale is highly exaggerated.

A water table has a seasonal rise and fall. There is a lag between the time of maximum infiltration and the highest water table level. In Britain, for example, the highest rates of infiltration occur in the winter but the water table does not reach its highest level until spring (Figure 3.6) when infiltration rates are lower, because infiltration is a relatively slow process, and it takes time for water to reach the saturated zone.

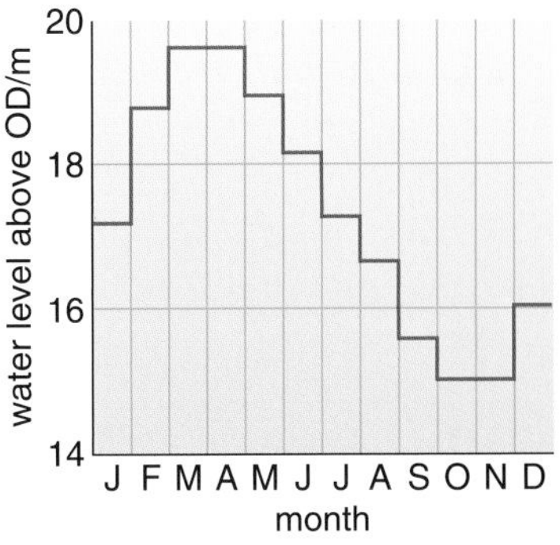

3.4 Groundwater movement

Groundwater flows underground in response to elevation differences (downwards) and pressure differences (from areas of high pressure to areas of low pressure). Near the water table, this means that groundwater usually flows 'downhill', i.e. from a higher level to a lower level, just as it would on the surface. The difference in energy between two points that are l metres apart horizontally on a sloping water table is determined by the difference in height (h) between them (Figure 3.7). This height is called the **head** of water. The slope of the water table is called the **hydraulic gradient** and is defined as h/l. The rate of groundwater movement (Q; the volume of water flowing in unit time, with units of $m^3 s^{-1}$) is related to the hydraulic gradient by **Darcy's law** (Box 3.1):

$$Q = KAh/l \tag{3.1}$$

In Equation 3.1, K is the **hydraulic conductivity** and is defined as the volume of water that will flow through a unit cross-sectional area of rock per unit time, under a unit hydraulic gradient and at a specified temperature. The units of hydraulic conductivity are metres per second ($m s^{-1}$) or metres per day. A is the cross-sectional area at right angles to the flow path.

The hydraulic conductivity depends on the properties of the rock that allow water to flow through it (its permeability) and also on the properties of the water. Unlike

Figure 3.6 Long-term mean monthly water level in an observation well at Dalton Holme, in Yorkshire. The water table is at its highest level in March and April.

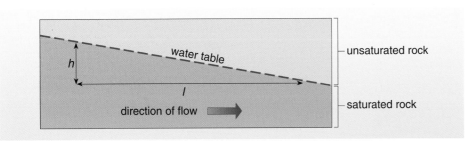

Figure 3.7 The flow of water through a permeable rock below the water table; h is the change in height of the water table, the head of water over a horizontal distance l, so that h/l is the hydraulic gradient.

Box 3.1 Henry Darcy

Darcy's law is named after Henry Darcy, who was born in Dijon in France in 1803. He trained as an engineer, and worked to solve the problem of providing drinking water in Dijon, which at the time had no reliable and safe supply. Darcy designed a water supply system for the city from a large spring 10 km away, piped to standpipes in the city, providing Dijon with its first good water supply.

Darcy also carried out experiments into the science of water flow and derived the relationship between the speed of flow and the hydraulic gradient which is now known as Darcy's law. This was published in 1856, together with his work on water supply, under the title *Les Fontaines Publiques de la Ville de Dijon*.

hydraulic conductivity, permeability is an intrinsic property of the rock, so it is the same whatever the nature of the fluid flowing through the rock — whether water, as in this instance, or oil or gas. The hydraulic conductivity (K), however, depends on the density and viscosity of the fluid, so it will vary accordingly. When the fluid is water, the most important factor that affects the hydraulic conductivity is temperature. For example, an increase in water temperature from 5 °C to about 30 °C will double the hydraulic conductivity and, from Darcy's law, will therefore double the speed at which the groundwater flows.

Rocks can be divided into two broad categories — permeable and impermeable — on the basis of their hydraulic conductivity. Rocks generally regarded as permeable have hydraulic conductivities of 1 m per day or more.

Hydraulic conductivity is proportional to permeability (permeability is discussed in greater detail in Section 3.6). So from Darcy's law (Equation 3.1) it can be deduced that in a rock of constant hydraulic conductivity (K), and hence of constant permeability for a given fluid, the rate (Q) at which the groundwater flows will increase as the hydraulic gradient (h/l, the slope of the water table) increases.

Groundwater flows in the direction of the hydraulic gradient (the maximum slope of the water table) at least for groundwater near the top of the saturated zone and where the rock is isotropic (has similar properties in all directions). If there are fissures, for example, and these are in a different orientation to the hydraulic gradient, the direction of flow will be greatly affected by the fissure orientation. Groundwater flow directions can be deduced from contour maps of the water table, as the direction of maximum slope is at right-angles to the water table contours. In Figure 3.8 directions of flow are added to the water table contour map in Figure 3.5a. In Question 3.2 we deduced that the water table in this area sloped down to the north-east, so the direction of groundwater flow was also to the north-east.

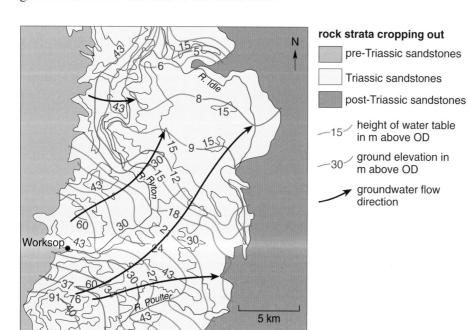

rock strata cropping out

- pre-Triassic sandstones
- Triassic sandstones
- post-Triassic sandstones

—15— height of water table in m above OD

—30— ground elevation in m above OD

→ groundwater flow direction

Figure 3.8   Direction of groundwater flow in the Triassic sandstones in Nottinghamshire. This figure covers the same area as Figure 3.5. The groundwater flows at right-angles to the water table contours, i.e. in the direction of slope of the water table.

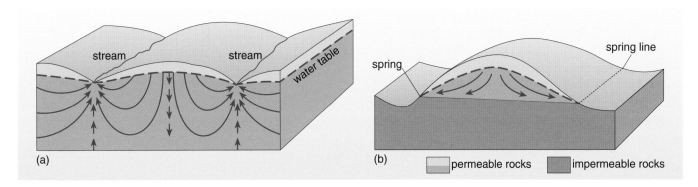

Figure 3.9 The direction of flow of groundwater at depth is not parallel to the water table; instead, water moves in a curved path, converging towards a point of discharge. In (a) the rock is uniformly permeable, and the water discharges into streams in the valleys; it may approach the stream from below. In (b) the hill is capped by a permeable rock which is underlain by an impermeable rock. The water is diverted laterally by the impermeable rock, and springs result where the boundary between the permeable and impermeable rocks intersects the ground surface.

This flow of groundwater in the direction of the slope of the water table is only part of the picture, for groundwater is also in motion at greater depths, where it generally moves in a curved path rather than a straight line when seen in cross-section (Figure 3.9), towards a stream or river, a spring, or even a well. This path is the result of movement towards an area of discharge, such as the stream.

In addition to the natural discharge at streams, rivers or springs, groundwater can be extracted from wells. The water table around a well from which water is being pumped will fall, forming a **cone of depression** (Figure 3.10). The shape and extent of the cone of depression depend on the hydraulic conductivity of the rock, the rate of pumping, and the duration of pumping. The difference in height between the water table before pumping and the level of water in the well during pumping is called the **drawdown**.

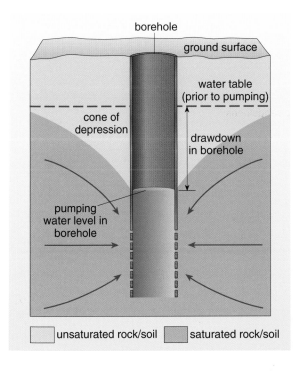

Figure 3.10 The water table is drawn down into a cone of depression around a pumped well. The diameter of the borehole is exaggerated.

At a coast, groundwater normally discharges into the sea because the water table slopes down towards sea level (Figure 3.11). Rocks under the sea, however, are generally saturated with seawater (saline groundwater). The boundary between fresh groundwater and saline groundwater usually slopes downward inland from the coast, with denser saline groundwater wedging under the less dense fresh groundwater below the land. The depth below sea level of the interface between fresh and saline groundwater at any point (h_2 on Figure 3.11) depends on the height of the water table above sea level (h_1). Along this interface the pressures due to the head of denser saline water and the less dense fresh water must balance. This means that the depth of the saline water below sea level (h_2) is about forty times the height of the water table above sea level (h_1). (The 'forty' comes from the difference in densities of fresh water and seawater.) So if the water table near a coast is, say, 5 m above sea level (that is, $h_1 = 5$ m), then the depth to the saline groundwater below the water table should be:

$$h_1 + h_2 = 5 + (40 \times 5) = 205 \text{ m} \qquad (3.2)$$

If the densities of the fresh or saline water vary, so will the 40 : 1 ratio of h_2 to h_1. This can happen where brackish waters form the interface with fresh water, because the interface between fresh groundwater and saline groundwater is usually not as sharp as is implied in Figure 3.11. Instead there is normally a zone, at least a few metres in thickness, where the fresh and saline groundwaters mix. The water in this zone is less saline than seawater; that is, it is brackish water. Also the level of the sea rises and falls with the tides, and there are variations in the rate of discharge of fresh groundwater to the sea. Factors such as these bring about changes in the position of the interface, and can promote mixing of fresh water and seawater. Figure 3.12 shows a zone of mixing between 200 m and 500 m wide off the coast of Florida.

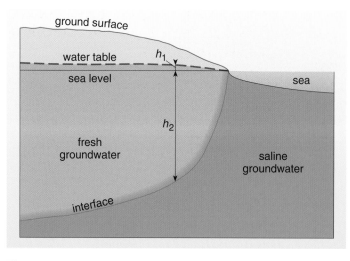

Figure 3.11   A cross-section illustrating the relationship between fresh groundwater and saline groundwater at a coast. The vertical scale is exaggerated.

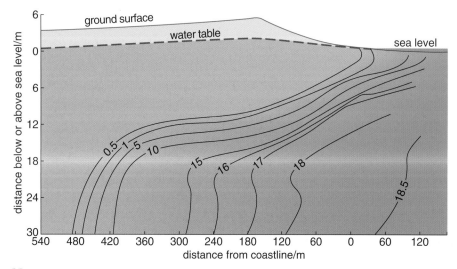

Figure 3.12   Mixing at the fresh groundwater/saline groundwater interface at Biscayne Bay, Florida. The contour values are chloride concentrations in grams per litre. The 18.5 g l⁻¹ contour represents seawater, and the 0.5 g l⁻¹ contour fresh water. Intermediate values result from the mixing of seawater and fresh water.

Seawater intrusion into wells can become a problem where large amounts of groundwater are extracted near a coast, so that saline groundwater moves inland. This is called a **saline intrusion**. If the water table is lowered by high rates of extraction (h_1 is reduced), the position of the interface between the fresh and saline groundwater rises (h_2 is reduced), so the wells may eventually fill with saline water and become useless for supplying fresh water. These problems can become acute on small islands, where a lens-shaped body of fresh groundwater usually overlies saline groundwater (Figure 3.13).

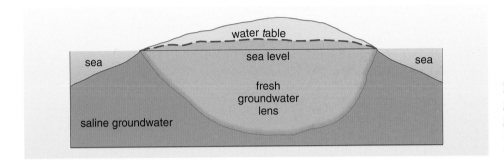

Figure 3.13 Fresh groundwater and saline groundwater below an island. A lens-shaped body of fresh water occurs below the island.

Saline intrusion along coasts can be controlled by limiting the rate at which groundwater is removed so that the water table remains above sea level and slopes down towards the coast. Providing the hydraulic gradient is seawards, fresh groundwater will flow in this direction, preventing further saline intrusion. This method of control is practised in eastern England. Saline intrusion can also be controlled by injecting fresh water into the ground. This can either be surplus water collected during wet months or water of low quality which would otherwise be discharged into the sea. The water is injected into the ground by secondary wells situated between the main extraction wells and the coast. Sewage effluent is used to control saline intrusions by this method on the western coast of the United States and in Israel.

3.5 Porosity

The amount of water that a rock can store depends on its **porosity**, which is the proportion of the volume of the rock that consists of pores:

$$\text{porosity (\%)} = \frac{\text{pore volume}}{\text{total volume}} \times 100\% \tag{3.3}$$

The principal factors that control porosity are grain size and shape, the degree of sorting (a well-sorted sediment has a narrow range of grain size), the extent to which cement occupies the pore spaces of grains and the amount of fracturing. Figure 3.14 illustrates how porosity varies with the degree of sorting and with the grain shape in unconsolidated sediments (sediments that have not been compacted or cemented). Unconsolidated sediments with rounded grains of uniform size (i.e. perfectly sorted) are the most porous (Figure 3.14a). Sediments decrease in porosity as the angularity of the grains increases because the grains can pack more closely together, the bumps of some grains fitting into indentations in others (Figure 3.14c). The porosity is also lower if the sediment is poorly sorted, because small grains can occupy the spaces between larger grains (Figure 3.14b).

Question 3.3

(a) Why is the sample in Figure 3.14a a well-sorted sediment, and why are Figures 3.14b and c poorly sorted sediments?

(b) Which are more porous — well-sorted sediments or poorly sorted sediments?

(c) Given similar degrees of sorting, how does porosity vary with the roundness of the grains?

(d) Estimate the porosity of the sediments in Figures 3.14a to d, selecting a value from the following ranges for each: less than 10%; 10–20%; 20–30%; 30–40%.

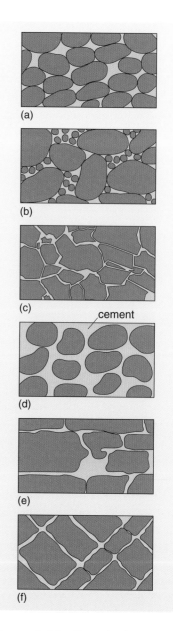

(a)

(b)

(c)

cement

(d)

(e)

(f)

Consolidated (compacted and/or cemented) sedimentary rocks, and igneous and metamorphic rocks are usually less porous than unconsolidated sediments (Table 3.1). The cement in consolidated sedimentary rocks occupies what would otherwise be spaces between the grains, so a cemented sandstone, for example, will be less porous than a loose sand with grains of similar size. Igneous and metamorphic rocks generally have very low porosity, because of their interlocking crystals. However, there are volcanic rocks that contain gas bubbles and some of these have high porosities.

The porosity of rocks may be increased by processes that occur *after* the rocks have formed. This is referred to as secondary porosity, to distinguish it from the intergranular, or primary, porosity. One type of secondary porosity is fracture porosity, caused by cracks in rocks (Figure 3.14f). Another type of secondary porosity is solution porosity, which develops where part of a rock has been dissolved, leaving open spaces (Figure 3.14e). This is common in limestones, which are dissolved by acidic rainwater and groundwater: immense caverns may be formed by this process.

Question 3.4

In broad terms, how does porosity vary with the grain size of (a) unconsolidated sediments and (b) consolidated sediments?

Figure 3.14 Porosity in unconsolidated sediments ((a) to (c)): (a) is well sorted, having high porosity; (b) is poorly sorted having low porosity; (c) has angular grains and low porosity; and in consolidated rocks ((d) to (f)): (d) has porosity diminished by cementation; (e) has solution porosity as it has partially dissolved; (f) has fracture porosity. (a)–(d) show vertical sections 1 cm across, (e) and (f) are 1 m across.

So how fast does water flow underground? Dividing both sides of Darcy's law (Equation 3.1) by A gives:

$$q = Kh/l \tag{3.4}$$

where q is the **specific discharge**, the volume of water flowing through unit cross-sectional area, i.e. Q/A. The actual speed of groundwater flow (v) is given by:

$$v = q/n \tag{3.5}$$

where n is the porosity of the rock. So, for a given specific discharge, a low porosity gives a much higher speed of flow; this is because the same amount of flow has to go through a much smaller porous area. For example, water flowing through a porous sandstone flows more slowly than water flowing through a granite or limestone when the porosity is provided by just one or two narrow fissures.

Table 3.1   Porosities and hydraulic conductivities for various rocks and sediments.

Geological material	Grain size/mm	Porosity (%)	Hydraulic conductivity/m per day
Unconsolidated sediments			
clay	0.0005 to 0.002	45 to 60	less than 10^{-2}
silt	0.002 to 0.06	40 to 50	10^{-2} to 1
sand	0.06 to 2	30 to 40	1 to 5×10^2
gravel	2 to 64	25 to 35	5×10^2 to 1×10^4
Consolidated sedimentary rocks			
shale	fine	5 to 15	5×10^{-8} to 5×10^{-6}
sandstone	medium	5 to 30	10^{-4} to 10*
limestone	variable	10^{-1} to 30* (solution porosity)	10^{-5} to 10*
Igneous and metamorphic rocks			
basalt	fine	10^{-3} to 1 (up to 50 if vesicular)	3×10^{-4} to 3*
granite	coarse	10^{-4} to 1 (up to 10 if fractured)	3×10^{-4} to 1*
slate	fine	10^{-3} to 1	10^{-8} to 10^{-5}
schist	medium	10^{-3} to 1	10^{-7} to 10^{-1}

*Values at the higher end of the range occur where there is secondary porosity or permeability.

The speed of flow in rocks is extremely slow in comparison with surface flow, even for rocks with high hydraulic conductivities. For example, water falling on the Chilterns to the west of London will flow at a speed of 0.1 to 1 m s^{-1} in a river, taking a few days to reach London. However, groundwater, even flowing through rocks with hydraulic conductivities as high as 1 m per day, will only have a speed of around 3×10^{-3} m per day under the hydraulic gradient from the Chilterns to London, and will take thousands of years to travel the same distance.

3.6   Permeability

It is important to distinguish clearly between porosity and permeability. Porosity is a measure of *how much* water can be stored in a rock, whereas permeability is a measure of the properties of a rock which determine *how easily* water and other fluids can *flow* through it (see Section 3.4). Permeability depends on the extent to which pores are *interconnected*.

Table 3.1 gives the porosity and hydraulic conductivity of various geological materials. As hydraulic conductivity depends on permeability, the values in the last column could be said to represent relative permeabilities. However, hydraulic conductivities rather than permeabilities are given in the table, because these can be used to calculate flow rates using Darcy's law (Equation 3.1).

For unconsolidated sediments, the finer-grained silts and clays are less permeable than the coarser sands and gravels, even though they are more porous (Table 3.1). There are two major reasons for this: first, the smaller grain sizes in silt and clay result in a greater surface area of particles relative to volume, so water tends to be held in the pores by surface tension; and second, the platy and angular shape of clay particles means that they tend to interlock and isolate the spaces between them, which further inhibits the movement of water through the sediment.

Which three of the sediments and rocks depicted in Figure 3.14 should have the higher permeabilities and which should have the lowest permeability?

Rocks that are highly permeable must be porous and have interconnected pores; so the examples in Figures 3.14a, e and f, should have higher permeabilities (even though Figures 3.14e and f have a fairly low *porosity*). Rocks with a low permeability must have very few, or isolated pores, so the water cannot move through the rock, and the example in Figure 3.14d in which original pore space is filled by cement should have the lowest permeability.

Usually, consolidated and cemented sedimentary rocks (and igneous and metamorphic rocks) are not very permeable, but sometimes processes such as solution or fracturing create *secondary permeability*. The higher hydraulic conductivities of some of the igneous, metamorphic and consolidated sedimentary rocks in Table 3.1 are mainly due to secondary permeability caused by fracturing or for limestone, solution.

3.7 Aquifers

A layer of rock that is sufficiently porous to store water, and permeable enough to allow water to flow through it, is called an **aquifer**. Consolidated porous and permeable rocks, for example, sandstone and limestone, can form important and extensive aquifers (e.g. Figure 3.15). Unconsolidated sands and gravels may also be good aquifers because they are relatively porous and very permeable, but in the UK their saturated thickness is usually quite small and they have limited storage, so they are not important aquifers.

Figure 3.15 An outcrop of the Chalk, showing the fractures that gives the rock its high permeability.

Although the porosity of an aquifer is a measure of the amount of water stored within the pores or fissures, it does not provide a direct measure of the amount of water that may be *recovered* by pumping or drainage. This is because a proportion of the water is always retained around the individual grains by surface tension, and this is known as the **specific retention**.

The **specific yield** is the maximum amount of water that can be recovered. Figure 3.16 illustrates how specific yield, specific retention and porosity vary with grain size for unconsolidated sediments. The relationship between specific yield, specific retention and porosity is expressed by the equation:

$$\text{specific yield} = \text{porosity} - \text{specific retention} \qquad (3.6)$$

All three terms in the equation are expressed as *percentages* of the total volume of the rock. The specific retention decreases with increasing grain size in unconsolidated sediments (Figure 3.16). (A few large particles would have a smaller total surface area than a lot of smaller particles occupying the same volume, and a smaller surface area retains less water by surface tension.) This means that less water is retained in coarse-grained sediments. However, the specific yield is greatest for medium-grained sediments (sands), rather than for coarse-grained sediments, because porosity decreases with increasing grain size.

The **exploitable storage** of water in an aquifer is the *volume* of water it will yield:

$$\text{exploitable storage} = V \times \frac{Y}{100} \qquad (3.7)$$

where V is the volume of the aquifer that is being exploited, and Y the specific yield. It is important to distinguish between the specific yield (a percentage of the volume of the rock) and the exploitable storage (a volume of water).

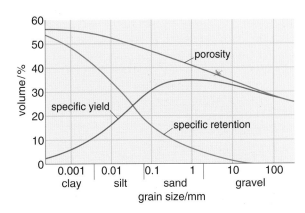

Figure 3.16   Relationships between porosity, specific retention and specific yield with variation in grain size for *unconsolidated sediments*. The grain size scale is not linear; each division corresponds to a factor of ten change in grain size. The lines on this graph are best-fit curves drawn through scattered points; you should not ascribe any degree of precision to them.

Question 3.5

Pumping from an unconsolidated aquifer lowered the water table by an average of 5 m over an area of 8×10^5 m².

(a) If the porosity of the aquifer averages 37% and the specific retention is 7%, calculate the specific yield of the rock.

(b) From this value, calculate the volume of water that was actually removed.

(c) From Figure 3.16, what type of rock is indicated by the data in (a)?

[Handwritten annotations:]
$V = 5 \times 8 \times 10^5 = .4 \times 10^{6} \text{ m}^3$
$Y = 37\% - 7\% = 30\%$
$\text{expl. s} = .4 \times 10^6 \times \frac{30}{100}$
$= .4 \times 10^4 \times 30$
$= 120 \times 10^4$
$= 1.2 \times 10^6 \text{ m}^3$

There are two types of aquifer, unconfined and confined, distinguished on the basis of their geological location in relation to the position of the saturated zone.

Unconfined aquifers crop out at the ground surface. The water table is the top of the saturated zone in an unconfined aquifer, and water normally has to be pumped to the surface except where the water table actually intersects the surface of the ground and forms a spring (Figure 3.17). A thin impermeable layer sometimes occurs locally in an aquifer, and this may support a small **perched aquifer**, separated from the main water table (see Figure 3.17).

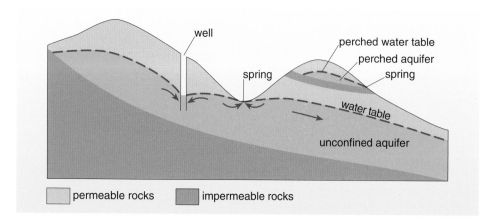

Figure 3.17 Unconfined and perched aquifers. Water discharges at the springs. Water extracted from the well causes drawdown to form a cone of depression in the water table around the well. The arrows show the directions in which groundwater flows. Water is not shown in the impermeable rock below the aquifer because although it is in the saturated zone, the water moves too slowly to be economically recoverable.

Confined aquifers are separated from the ground surface by an impermeable layer (as in most of Figure 3.18) and are generally at greater depths than unconfined aquifers. Pressures in confined aquifers may be sufficient for the water in wells that penetrate the aquifer to discharge naturally at the surface without pumping.

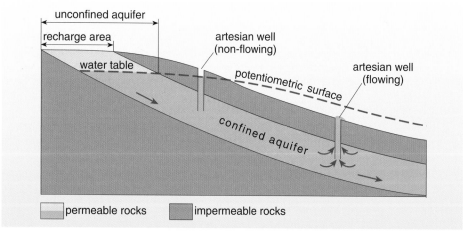

Figure 3.18 The relationship between unconfined and confined aquifers. The arrows show the directions of groundwater flow. To the left of the diagram the aquifer crops out and is unconfined; the aquifer is recharged in this area. The unconfined area extends to the intersection of the water table with the overlying impermeable rock. Here the potentiometric surface is also the water table.

Water in confined aquifers is called artesian water and a well that penetrates a confined aquifer is called an **artesian well**. The height to which water will rise in a well is called the potentiometric level and the **potentiometric surface** is an imaginary surface joining the potentiometric levels for a confined aquifer. For an unconfined aquifer, the potentiometric surface is the water table. The gradient of the potentiometric surface in a confined aquifer can be used to calculate groundwater flow rates, just as water table gradients are used to work out flow rates in unconfined aquifers using Darcy's law (Equation 3.1). The potentiometric surface is usually curved, with a convex upper slope, because the saturated thickness is decreasing in the direction of groundwater flow and so the hydraulic gradient has to steepen to maintain constant flow through a smaller saturated thickness. Even if the head is insufficient for water to rise to the surface, water in artesian wells rises above the top of the aquifer.

For artesian pressure to be maintained, the water that flows from the well must be replaced by water that infiltrates into the aquifer where it crops out and is thus unconfined (that is, the same aquifer can be confined in one area and unconfined in another — see Figure 3.18). This area of outcrop is called the **recharge area** of the aquifer.

Figure 3.19 An oasis in the desert.

Naturally flowing artesian springs occur where the potentiometric surface is above the ground surface. An **oasis** in the desert is a natural spring, where groundwater is discharged at the surface (Figure 3.19). Oases can occur where the crest of a fold in a confined aquifer is intersected by the ground surface, or as an artesian spring where water can rise to the surface along a fault where the potentiometric surface is at or above ground level (Figure 3.20). The water discharged at oases is often recharged in mountainous areas, which may be a great distance away. Therefore the groundwater in large, confined aquifers may be of considerable age; i.e. much time has elapsed since the water fell as rain. An example is the Nubian sandstone aquifer, a confined aquifer that underlies a large part of northern Africa. Artesian water in this aquifer has been dated using carbon isotopes, giving ages of up to 40 000 years. Such dates make it possible to calculate groundwater speeds and, from Darcy's law, the hydraulic conductivity of the aquifer.

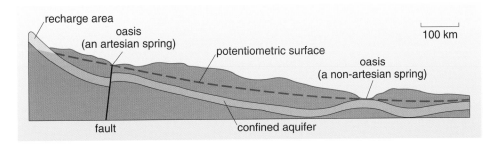

Figure 3.20 An aquifer can give rise to oases in desert regions, either by seepage up fault planes (an artesian spring) or by actual exposure of the aquifer at the surface due to folding or by erosion of the surface (a non-artesian spring).

Because groundwater flows so slowly, the water in large artesian aquifers is not always renewed as fast as it is extracted. Also, the water may have accumulated when the climate was very different: the oldest Nubian artesian water, for example, fell as rain at a time when the climate was cooler and wetter. Since then the area has become much warmer and drier, so the aquifer is recharging much more slowly. Under such circumstances, water in some large artesian aquifers in semi-arid regions is in practice a *non-renewable resource*.

All the same, in the *short* term, it is possible to '*mine*' water from an aquifer (which will be replaced very slowly or not at all), because the volume of water stored in an aquifer is usually large compared with the amount being removed. In the longer term, however, mining water will have adverse effects, including a lowered water table, a need for more expensive pumping from greater depths, a reduced flow to springs and rivers, and possibly a deterioration in groundwater quality.

In general, the rate at which water is removed from an aquifer should not be allowed to reduce the average water table level or have other adverse effects. The maximum quantity of water that can be safely removed from an aquifer annually is termed the **safe yield** for the aquifer. The consequences of extraction of groundwater above the safe yield from the aquifer below London are examined in Box 3.2.

Box 3.2 The fall and rise of groundwater under London

London is underlain by a confined aquifer, the Chalk, which is a limestone of Cretaceous age, and the overlying Tertiary Basal Sands. The aquifer is folded, with the deepest part below central London (Figure 3.21), and is overlain by Tertiary clay. This aquifer is recharged on the Chalk outcrops in the Chiltern Hills, Berkshire Downs and North Downs. Under natural conditions, groundwater flows through the confined aquifer and discharges through wells in the Thames Valley. The Trafalgar Square fountains in London used to rise naturally by artesian flow.

During the 19th and 20th centuries water was pumped from the aquifer for the public water supply, industrial and commercial uses. Long-term extraction and high extraction rates caused the potentiometric surface in the aquifer to fall to around −80 m OD by the mid-1960s (Figure 3.22). The fall in the potentiometric surface:

- stopped the natural discharge to the Thames estuary below London;

- led to saline intrusion from the Thames estuary below London;

- reduced the flow of springs from the Chalk outcrop and reduced river flows;

- increased the rate of flow of groundwater through the confined aquifer, because of the steeper hydraulic gradient;

- allowed water to drain from the clays overlying the confined aquifer, causing shrinkage, and as a result the ground surface subsided by up to several tens of centimetres.

Some of these consequences may seem to be undesirable but they were offset by the ready availability of groundwater below London during the 19th and 20th centuries, which played an important role in the economic development of the city.

As London expanded, higher buildings with deep basements and foundations were constructed. Also, expansion of the public transport system and other services led to the construction of deep tunnels to avoid using surface land. These foundations and tunnels were designed for the low groundwater levels and clay properties at that time.

Since the mid-1960s reduced extraction rates have led to a steady rise in groundwater levels (Figure 3.22). The reduction is attributed to: industrial decentralization from London, the introduction of licensing controls on private extractions, and the high cost of pumping.

It became a concern that if groundwater levels continue to rise, underground structures in London could be endangered by flooding of basements and tunnels, increased water pressures, swelling of clay and chemical attack on buried concrete and steel —

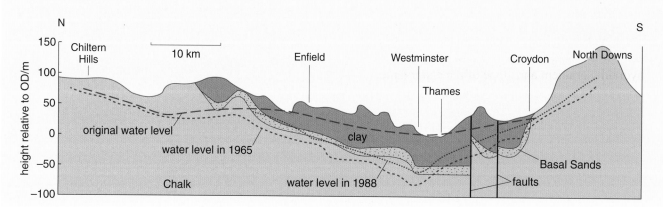

Figure 3.21 A geological cross-section through London. There is a large vertical exaggeration on this section (see vertical and horizontal scales). Negative height values are depths below OD. The Chalk and the Basal Sands form a confined aquifer, beneath impermeable clay layers. The vertical black lines to the south of the River Thames are faults.

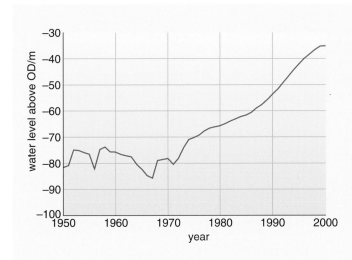

an environmental problem for the future. However, by 1999 the groundwater level seemed to have stabilized (Figure 3.22).

Figure 3.22 The water level in a well at Trafalgar Square, 1950–2000. In 1850 the level was about −22 m OD, falling gradually to about −80 m OD in 1950. Since 1972 the water level has risen, stabilizing at around −34 m OD by 1999.

3.8 Summary of Chapter 3

1   The rate at which water infiltrates into the ground depends on the permeability of the rocks and the state of the ground surface. Below the ground surface there is an unsaturated zone which has air in the pore spaces, and a saturated zone which has all the pores filled with water. The water table is the boundary between the unsaturated zone and the saturated zone, and is the level at which water stands in wells. Water below the water table is called groundwater. The water table follows the topography of the ground surface but with more gentle gradients.

2   Groundwater will flow in response to differences in elevation and pressure. Darcy's law relates the rate of the groundwater movement (Q) to the hydraulic conductivity (K), the cross-sectional area (A) and to the hydraulic gradient or slope of the water table (h/l):

$Q = KAh/l$

The hydraulic conductivity depends on the permeability of the rock and on the properties of the water. Water generally flows in the direction of the hydraulic gradient and slope of the water table.

3   A cone of depression is formed in the water level around a well from which water is being pumped. The difference in height between the water table before pumping and the water level in the well during pumping is called the drawdown.

4   There is usually saline groundwater under the land at a coast, with a wedge of denser saline groundwater under the fresh groundwater. The depth to the saline groundwater depends on the height of the water table above sea level and on the densities of the fresh and saline water.

5   The porosity of a rock is the proportion of its volume that consists of pores:

$$\text{porosity (\%)} = \frac{\text{pore volume}}{\text{total volume}} \times 100\%$$

Porosity is a measure of how much water a rock can store. The permeability of a rock is a measure of the properties of the rock which determine how easily water can flow through it. The porosity and permeability are generally greater in unconsolidated sedimentary rocks, particularly sands and gravels, than in consolidated sedimentary, igneous or metamorphic rocks. Both porosity and permeability can be increased by processes that occur after the formation of the rock, such as solution or fracturing. These are called secondary porosity and secondary permeability.

6   An aquifer is a body of rock that can store water, and through which water can flow. For a rock to be an aquifer it must be sufficiently porous and it must be permeable. Igneous and metamorphic rocks seldom make good aquifers unless they have both secondary porosity and secondary permeability.

7   The proportion of water that can be recovered from a saturated aquifer is known as the specific yield. This is less than the total amount of water stored in the aquifer (represented by the porosity) because some of the water is retained by surface tension around the individual grains (specific retention). Specific yield, like porosity, is expressed as a percentage of the total volume of the rock. The highest porosities are found in fine-grained sediments, but the greatest specific yields are in medium-grained sediments. The exploitable storage of a saturated aquifer is the volume of water it will give up when pumped or allowed to drain.

8   Aquifers can be unconfined or confined. Unconfined aquifers crop out at the ground surface; water normally has to be pumped to the surface from the water table in these aquifers. Confined aquifers are separated from the ground surface by an impermeable layer. Water in confined aquifers is called artesian water, and wells that penetrate confined aquifers are called artesian wells. The water in an artesian well may be under sufficient pressure to reach the surface of the ground without pumping (a flowing artesian well).

9   The potentiometric surface is an imaginary surface joining the heights to which water will rise. For an unconfined aquifer, the potentiometric surface is the water table.

10 The safe yield of an aquifer is the maximum rate of extraction of water that does not produce a long-term decline in the average water table level or have any other adverse effect, such as a significant reduction in the flow to springs and rivers. Exceeding the safe yield (i.e. 'mining' groundwater) would necessitate pumping from progressively greater depths to obtain water, and might lead to a reduced flow to springs and rivers, and a deterioration in water quality.

SURFACE WATER

4.1 Springs

We have seen that where precipitation reaches the ground, some runs off the surface into streams and rivers and some of it infiltrates, passing through the soil. Water that reaches the water table to become groundwater may eventually re-emerge at the surface as springs where the water table intersects the surface. Almost all streams and rivers have springs or seepages as their ultimate source, or are fed by them at various points along their courses.

In Section 3.7 we looked at artesian springs which are associated with confined aquifers. These are most obvious on land, but can also occur on the sea bed, a fact long known to sailors who have used them to fill up with fresh water while still at sea. In such cases, an aquifer has its recharge area on land but extends beyond the coast to underlie the sea bed, where if the geology and topography are favourable, and the aquifer intersects the sea bed, fresh water may emerge.

Most springs, however, are ordinary water-table springs, and these can be of several different kinds depending on the geological setting:

- *Valley springs* develop in valleys where the ground surface intersects the water table (Figure 3.17). In southern England, a number of seasonal springs occur in the Chalk valleys when the water table rises during a wet winter. These temporary streams are called *bournes* (Figure 4.1), reflected in some of the place names in the area, e.g. Winterbourne Stoke in Dorset. These bournes dry up in summer, when the water table drops below the ground surface.

- *Stratum springs* form where the downward flow of groundwater is prevented by an underlying impermeable layer of rock, which can result in a line of springs emerging at the boundary between the two layers (Figures 3.9b, 3.17 and 4.2).

- *Solution channel springs* typically occur in limestone districts where groundwater has created caves and channels by dissolving calcium carbonate along bedding planes and fractures, and then returned to the surface where impermeable strata prevent further downwards migration.

Figure 4.1 The River Thames about 1 km from its source in Gloucestershire. Here the river is a bourne arising from a valley spring — the photograph was taken when the water table was high in spring. At the end of summer when the water table is lower, there is no flow here, and the River Thames rises about 3 km downstream.

Figure 4.2 This desert in Jordan has sparse vegetation, except at the boundary between a permeable sandstone and an underlying impermeable granite, where there are stratum springs. These are marked by the line of vegetation about half way up the cliff face.

4.2   River flow

The total land area drained by a river system, including all its tributaries, is called a river **catchment**. The water in a river comes not only from direct precipitation, springs and **overland flow** (i.e. water flowing across the ground surface, excluding that in streams and rivers; this is rare in temperate vegetated areas) but also from the underground flow of water, directly to the river. Part of this underground flow is **interflow**, that part of infiltration which moves through the unsaturated zone without penetrating to the main water table (Figure 4.3). It occurs because the permeability of the unsaturated zone tends to reduce with depth thereby restricting infiltration. The term also includes water that flows from any perched water tables in the unsaturated zone (Figure 3.17).

Below the water table, groundwater can discharge directly into a river, and this is called **baseflow** (Figure 4.3). The contribution of baseflow to river flow varies greatly with the geology and topography of the catchment and with the season. The baseflow contribution is low for a river in a catchment of impermeable rocks, where rainfall infiltrates slowly, and the overland flow is consequently high. In contrast, for rivers with a catchment of permeable rocks there may be no water from overland flow in the rivers. All of the river flow in this case will be baseflow. In Britain, baseflow usually forms a higher proportion of the total flow in summer than in winter, because evaporation is higher in summer and overland flow is therefore lower, whereas groundwater is released to rivers as baseflow more consistently throughout the year.

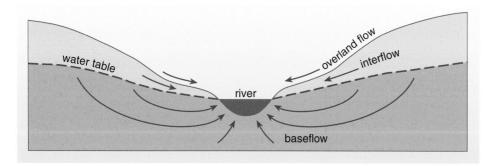

Figure 4.3   The discharge of a river comes from overland flow, interflow above the water table and groundwater baseflow. Arrows show directions of flow.

The water level in a river, called the **stage**, is easy to measure (Figure 4.4), whereas the **discharge** of a river, the volume of water that flows past a point in a certain time, cannot be measured directly. However, the measurement, or gauging, of river discharge is necessary for the calculation of surface water resources. Regularly recorded discharge values also give information about the maximum and minimum volumes of water flowing in the river, which is required for planning water supply schemes and for flood-control and hydroelectric projects. The discharge (Q) of a river is related to the speed of flow (v) by the equation:

$$Q = Av \tag{4.1}$$

where A is the cross-sectional area of the river.

The cross-sectional area of a river channel at a discharge measurement point is determined from measurements of the depth of the water taken at known intervals across the river. The speed of the flow can be measured using current meters; these have vanes that are turned by the water flowing past, the rate of

Figure 4.4 A post for monitoring water level (a 'stage' post) on the West Okement river, Devon. The level is recorded automatically inside the hut behind the stage post.

rotation giving the water speed. However, the speed is not constant from bank to bank or from the bed to the surface, so a number of speed measurements must be made at different depths at intervals across the river. In order to do this the river cross-section is divided into small areas, and the discharge within each area is calculated from the measured speeds (area × speed across that section). The total discharge is the sum of the individual discharges.

This method is very laborious, as many speed–depth measurements have to be made for each determination of discharge. However, once the discharge at a particular stage (water level) has been measured, the assumption can be made that for the same stage at that location, the discharge will be the same. This means that if the discharge in the river has been measured at different stages, so that the relationship between stage and discharge is known at that location, the river discharge can be estimated from measurement of stage alone; this is read directly from a post in the river. Figure 4.5 shows a **rating curve** for a river; it is a plot of discharge values measured at various stages, with a smooth curve drawn through the plotted points. The shapes of rating curves can vary considerably: they may be quite different from the curve in Figure 4.5.

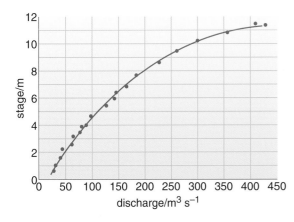

Figure 4.5 A river rating curve. A best-fit line is drawn through the measured values.

How accurately do you think the discharge can be estimated from the stage, using a rating curve?

Reasonably accurately, as most points lie fairly close to the curve. The differences arise from the errors in measuring the river cross-section and flow rates. Where possible, concrete weirs are built into the river at gauging stations to reduce the errors involved in using rating curves to estimate discharge (Figure 4.6). These have a straightforward cross-section, with either a horizontal surface, or a V-notch.

Figure 4.6 A horizontal concrete weir on the West Okement river, Devon. The weir reduces errors in estimating discharge from stage measurements.

A record of the discharge over time is called a **discharge hydrograph** (usually abbreviated to **hydrograph**). This is calculated from a stage hydrograph, a record of stage over time.

River discharge is related to the effective precipitation over the catchment. After precipitation begins, the discharge usually increases rapidly to a peak and then decreases more slowly (Figure 4.7). Initially the increased discharge comes from overland flow, then interflow, but these die away fairly soon after the rain stops falling, eventually leaving only the baseflow contribution to the river.

Hydrographs can be used to show short-term variations (recorded over a few days), such as how discharge from a catchment responds to individual rainstorms (Figure 4.7), or long-term variations (recorded over a year or more), illustrating a climatic regime. The resultant hydrographs are called short-period and long-period hydrographs, respectively. The shape of a hydrograph depends on several factors:

- *Short-term variations: the size and shape of the catchment area.* Generally, the larger the catchment, the higher the peak discharge for a given rainfall and the longer the time difference (lag) between rainfall maximum and river discharge maximum. The steepness of the slope of the ground is also significant, as gentle slopes produce a longer time difference because the water runs off more slowly.

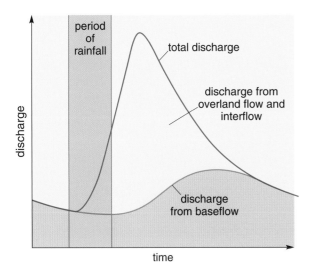

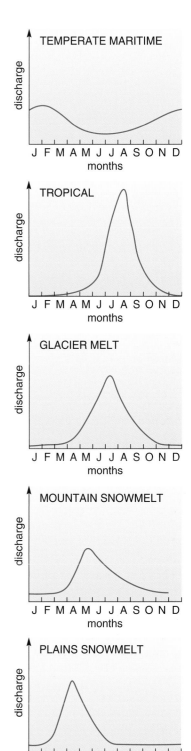

Figure 4.7 A short-period hydrograph before, during and after a rainstorm. There is a time difference ('lag') between the time of rainfall and the time of maximum discharge, and between maximum discharge and maximum baseflow. The slope of a hydrograph is usually steeper when a river is rising than when it is falling.

- *Short-term variations: vegetation and land use.* Vegetation cover and human use of the land affects hydrographs, as described in Box 4.1.

- *Short- to medium-term variations: the geology of the catchment*, particularly the permeability of the rocks. An impermeable catchment will produce higher peak discharges but lower flows at other times and respond more quickly than a permeable catchment. In a permeable catchment, with a greater baseflow contribution, there is less variation in discharge.

- *Long-term variations: climatic factors*, such as seasonal rainfall and melting snow.

Figure 4.8 shows the types of long-period hydrograph to be expected from different climatic regimes. (These hydrographs cover a year, whereas the hydrograph in Figure 4.7 is for a few days only.) In temperate maritime climates, rainfall occurs all the year, but as temperature is higher in summer, evaporation is also greater in summer, so there is a greater discharge in winter than in summer. Within the tropics and in the equatorial zone there are usually wet and dry seasons, or even two wet seasons (Figure 2.7, Section 2.2), and hydrographs are controlled by the effective rainfall pattern.

The other hydrographs in Figure 4.8 (glacier melt, mountain snowmelt and plains snowmelt) are dependent on seasonal *temperature*, in particular when it becomes warm enough to melt snow and ice. In the Northern Hemisphere, as melting takes place mainly in the summer, the peak discharges are in June or July. Melting of mountain snow starts earlier in the year, giving a peak discharge in May or June. Snowmelt from plains (the interior regions of large continents) depends on latitude, with the more southerly rivers having peak discharges in April, and more northerly rivers having a peak in June. River hydrographs are often a combination of one or more of the climatic regimes in Figure 4.8.

Figure 4.8 Theoretical yearly hydrographs for different climatic regimes in the Northern Hemisphere. The months of the year are indicated by their initial letters.

Box 4.1   Land use and river discharge

Changes made in the use of the land surface have varying effects on the overland flow and infiltration characteristics of a catchment, and so can change the river discharge pattern.

Plants, especially trees, intercept precipitation and prevent it reaching the ground. An area that is forested also usually has a thick layer of decaying vegetation on the ground, which absorbs water, so plants, and forests in particular, reduce overland flow to rivers (Figure 4.9a). The peak discharge is less in a forested area and the lag time is greater. Catchments of many upland reservoirs are forested, but as Figure 4.9a demonstrates, this may not be ideal for water supply, as afforestation reduces the total volume of water reaching a river, although it makes the flow more uniform.

Urbanization of land usually results in less infiltration and faster overland flow from buildings and roads, giving very high peak discharges on

hydrographs (Figure 4.9a) and sometimes the risk of flooding. To reduce this risk, and maintain the water table, balancing lakes are constructed in newly urbanized areas (such as Milton Keynes) to provide an area for increased infiltration.

If the ground is relatively impermeable, which can occur when the soil is frozen or the underlying rock is impermeable, lag time is reduced and peak discharge is increased (Figure 4.9b). The same effect occurs with heavy rainfall; with light rain there is time to infiltrate the ground, but heavier rainfall causes mostly overland flow (Figure 4.9c).

Draining wetlands or marshes removes water from such areas more quickly, increasing the peak flow and runoff volume. The rapid discharge of water reduces the time available for infiltration and may lower the water table, modifying the vegetation and changing the discharge characteristics of the area.

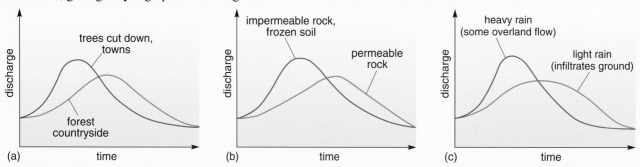

Figure 4.9   The effect of (a) change of land use, (b) underlying ground and rock type, and (c) rain intensity, on short-period river hydrographs responding to similar rainstorms.

Question 4.1

Figure 4.10 is a hydrograph, covering a period of a year.

(a) Which climatic regime or regimes would produce a hydrograph of this shape?

(b) What is the maximum discharge and how many times greater than the mean discharge is it?

(c) What might be the cause of the high discharge peaks?

The river represented in Figure 4.10 discharges more water in the winter, whereas demand for water is higher in the hotter summer. To satisfy the summer demand, water must be stored during the winter and spring.

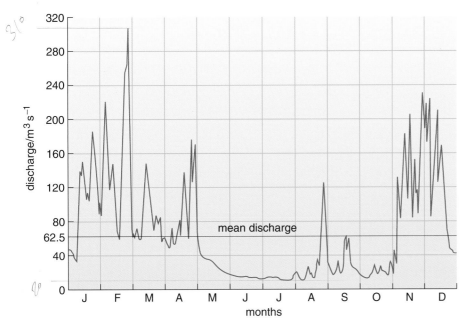

Figure 4.10   A hydrograph, for use with Questions 4.1 and 4.2. The horizontal line marks the mean discharge of 62.5 m³ s⁻¹ for this river over a long period.

Question 4.2

Estimate the percentage contributed by the baseflow to the discharge of the River Severn at Bewdley (Figure 4.10), for (a) the months November–April and (b) the months May–October. Give your answers to the nearest 10%. You may need to refer to Figure 4.7 to identify the baseflow component of the hydrograph.

4.3   Reservoirs

The simplest and oldest way of storing surface water is in reservoirs and this has been done for thousands of years. Most reservoirs are still built to increase water supplies, but some are also built for other purposes, especially for generating hydroelectric power and for protection against floods. The Tennessee River in the United States, for example, has reservoirs to trap and store water that would otherwise cause floods, the water being released when the height of the river falls to safe levels. The Aswan High Dam in Egypt is used both to generate electricity and reduce flooding, as well as to provide water for irrigation.

Most older reservoirs, particularly in the UK, are **direct supply reservoirs**; they store water for steady release by pipeline to the public supply. Many of the newer reservoirs are for **river regulation** (Box 4.2); stored water is released into rivers when the natural discharge is low, so that it can be abstracted for use further downstream. The river itself transports the water from the reservoir so a pipeline is unnecessary. Unregulated, the discharge in winter exceeds requirements, but by storing winter water the scheme provides more water in summer than would be naturally available in the river. The Clywedog reservoir on a tributary of the River Severn, for example, was built to store up to 50 million m³ of water in winter, releasing it during the summer. This is needed because, as Figure 4.10 shows, the summer discharge is only around 20 m³ s⁻¹ downstream at Bewdley, whereas in winter about 120 m³ s⁻¹ are discharged. Both direct supply reservoirs and river regulation reservoirs may be **pumped storage reservoirs**, which do not fill naturally from a river, but have water pumped up to them. Many of the reservoirs in the Thames Valley are pumped storage reservoirs.

Box 4.2 The Colorado River

The change in river discharge patterns caused by river regulation reservoirs can be seen on a long-period hydrograph of the Colorado River in the USA (Figure 4.11). The Colorado is a large river (its annual discharge is about ten times greater than the River Severn, Figure 4.10) and has great seasonal fluctuations: in 1920, for example, its discharge varied from 50 to 2600 m³ s⁻¹. This seasonal variation is caused by mountain snowmelt in the upper parts of the Colorado catchment in Wyoming, Colorado and Utah.

Downstream, the Colorado River flows through desert and its water is very important, but most of this flow was in the winter, when it was less useful

for irrigation. Annual flooding was also common. To regulate the river flow, prevent flooding and to generate hydroelectric power, dams were built on the Colorado to create reservoirs (Figure 4.12). The first major dam, the Hoover Dam (Figure 4.13), was completed in 1935, forming the reservoir of Lake Mead. This holds most of the spring snowmelt and prevents very high discharges and flooding.

● How did the discharge change after the creation of Lake Mead reservoir?

○ The peak discharge was reduced to about 800 m³ s⁻¹: much lower than previous highs of up to 2800 m³ s⁻¹ before 1935.

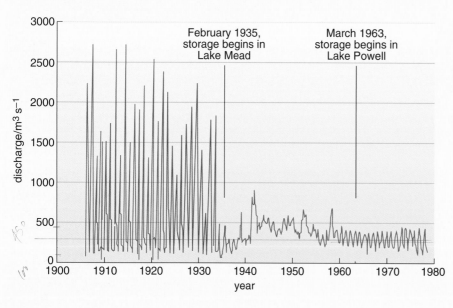

Figure 4.11 Hydrograph for the Colorado River in the south-western United States for 1906–79, measured downstream of the Hoover Dam. The reservoir behind the Hoover Dam is Lake Mead.

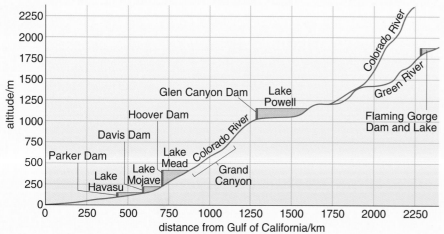

Figure 4.12 Longitudinal profile of the Colorado River and its major tributary, the Green River, showing the major dams and reservoirs.

Figure 4.13 The Hoover Dam and part of Lake Mead on the Colorado River.

○ How has Lake Mead affected the lower discharges of the Colorado?

○ These have increased, from typical values of $100\text{--}200\,m^3\,s^{-1}$ before 1935, to $300\text{--}500\,m^3\,s^{-1}$ from 1942 to 1955.

Raised lower discharges are because Lake Mead is a river regulation reservoir: water is released downstream into the river at a more constant rate than in the unregulated flow. Lake Mead is also a direct supply reservoir, supplying water by pipeline to eastern Nevada, and for hydroelectric power generation.

Even after the completion of Lake Mead there were still times when floodwaters filled the lake and were released downstream.

○ In which years, after 1935, did this happen?

○ There were peak discharges (although much lower than the pre-1935 peaks) in 1938, 1942, 1953 and 1958.

Another major reservoir, Lake Powell, was created upstream of Lake Mead in 1963 to trap this excess floodwater (Figures 4.11 and 4.12). Lake Powell is also used for water supply and hydroelectric power as well as river regulation. Since 1963, although there are still seasonal variations in flow, these are relatively small, with maximum flows of around $400\,m^3\,s^{-1}$ and minimum flows of around $200\,m^3\,s^{-1}$.

The multipurpose nature of the Colorado dams can cause particular problems. For example, although the dams have mostly eliminated the flooding along the lower Colorado, the reservoirs are often full in winter (with water being held for water supply use in summer) so no longer have the capacity to hold unexpected floodwaters.

The reservoirs trap most of the sediment behind the dams, which not only reduces the reservoir capacity, but also leaves the river below the dam lacking in nutrients and unable to support properly an aquatic ecosystem. The reservoirs are also polluted from heavy metals in the sediment (that would otherwise have been transported out to sea) and by oil, from recreational boats on the reservoirs. These factors have caused serious concerns about the environmental effects of big dams (Section 4.3.3).

4.3.1 Sites for reservoirs

The simplest way to create a reservoir is to build a dam across a river where it flows through a narrow, deep valley. This shape of valley would enable a considerable volume of water to be stored without flooding a large area of land or building a long dam. However, it is not always possible to find such a suitable site: a narrow, deep valley may not exist, or it may be too far from where the water is needed. A wide valley needing a long dam may have to be used, or even a flat lowland area that would need a low earth embankment surrounding most, if not all, of a shallow reservoir occupying a large area of land.

In practice, the following factors have to be considered when choosing a site for a water-supply reservoir:

1   an adequate supply of preferably high-quality water;
2   a minimum of detrimental effects on the environment;
3   sufficient elevation to provide a natural flow of water to the distribution system.

Once these general points are satisfied, the specific location of the reservoir requires:

4   a reasonably watertight reservoir base and sides;
5   no geological hazards such as instability of the sides of the valley or the likelihood of earthquakes;
6   a suitable site for the dam, preferably in a narrow valley.

The most important of these requirements are an adequate supply of water (1), preferably though not necessarily of high quality, and minimal environmental implications (2). All the other requirements can often be engineered, although it may be expensive to do so: water can be treated to improve its quality (1), or pumped to a higher level (3), and geological problems such as leakage (4) and instability (5) can be minimized.

The possibility of detrimental ecological or environmental effects can provoke much opposition to plans for new reservoirs, but if the need for a reservoir is great enough and there are no alternative areas, the reservoir is usually built. For example, the proposal to build the Aswan High Dam in the 1960s provoked opposition not only in Egypt but also world-wide, partly on the ground that it would drown the ancient temples of Abu Simbel. The dam was nevertheless constructed, and some of the temples were moved (Figure 4.14).

The reservoir requirements that the area should be watertight, have minimal geological hazards, and have a suitable site for a dam, all involve considering the area's geology. Watertightness is affected by the permeability of the underlying rocks, as well as by the geological structure of the area, the nature of any superficial deposits, and the position of the water table.

If the underlying rocks are permeable, water may be lost from the reservoir by infiltration. Rocks with low permeability, suitable for reservoir areas, include clay-rich rocks, and most igneous and metamorphic rocks, provided they are not too highly fractured. However, reservoirs are sometimes built in areas with less suitable, more permeable rocks, such as sandstone or limestone, if no more suitable rocks are available. Such areas can be made more watertight by lining the floor with clay or injecting concrete into permeable zones, although both methods are very expensive and only suitable for small areas.

Most valley floors are covered with superficial deposits such as gravel, clay or peat. These usually have to be removed from the dam site so that the dam can be given a strong

Figure 4.14   The Abu Simbel temples in Egypt, during their reconstruction in 1966. The temples were moved from an area that was submerged by the reservoir of Lake Nasser, behind the Aswan High Dam. Moving the temples was mainly financed by UNESCO.

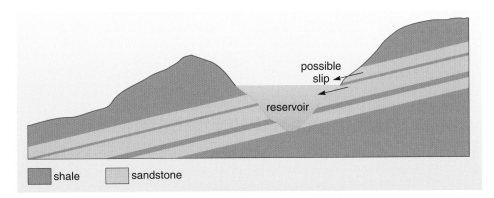

shale   sandstone

Figure 4.15 Water can be lost from a reservoir through bands of a permeable rock, such as sandstone, which dip away from a reservoir (left side of figure). Bands of shale provide planes on which saturated rocks can slide. Therefore if rocks dip towards the reservoir, as on the right side of the figure, there may be a danger of landslides into the reservoir. This danger is increased by the presence of the reservoir which raises the water table in the rocks on either side of the valley.

foundation in the underlying rock. Peat should be removed from the whole reservoir area as it is acidic and would affect the colour and quality of the water; but clays may be useful, as they are impermeable and can seal any underlying permeable rocks.

Problems caused by geological structures are not so easy to deal with. It is not usually possible to seal faults completely in the rocks under the area and some water may escape through them. If the rocks dip or are folded, water may be lost from the reservoir through the valley sides (Figure 4.15) or floor, or beneath the dam.

Reservoirs may contribute to the danger of landslides where a reservoir is sited on bedrock strata that dip towards the reservoir. The rocks on the right of the reservoir in Figure 4.15 are inclined towards it and consist of alternating sandstone and shale bands. The sandstones are permeable, and water in them percolates down to the shale bands. The shale bands are impermeable, so the water builds up above the shale until eventually it may act as a lubricant, allowing the sandstone above to slide downhill into the reservoir. This would displace a large volume of water and could cause flooding, the risk of damage and loss of life (Box 4.3).

Box 4.3   The Vaiont reservoir landslip

The Vaiont reservoir in Italy is in an area of limestones with marl bands (marl is a calcareous mudstone). The dam was completed in 1961 and was 262 m high. This was one of the highest dams in existence, and the considerable depth of water created, when the reservoir filled, raised the water table in the surrounding rocks and produced a large increase in pore pressure. This lubricated the beds of rock and, in 1963, after heavy rains, caused a large landslide which dumped enormous amounts of rock (around $2.7 \times 10^8\,\text{m}^3$) into the reservoir from the flanking hillside (Figure 4.16). A huge volume of water was displaced, which surged over the dam and also back up the valley, causing around 2500 deaths in nearby villages. Remarkably, the dam itself remained intact.

Figure 4.16   The Vaiont reservoir. The slipped material is at the far end of the reservoir, below the slip plane, an area of bare rock, which is light-coloured in this photograph.

4.3.2 Dams

To economize on constructional materials and costs, it is desirable to build a dam at a narrow part of a valley so that the dam can be kept as short as possible. The quantity of constructional materials needed to build dams, and their cost, can be enormous. The Aswan High Dam, built during the 1960s, cost £400 million for a 1.2 km dam. Though shorter than the Aswan High Dam, the longest dam in Britain, the Kielder Dam in Northumberland (Figure 4.17), which was completed in 1980, was part of a scheme costing £150 million.

Figure 4.17 The Kielder Dam on the River North Tyne in Northumberland under construction in 1980. It is an earth gravity dam, with a central clay core and a clay apron for watertightness.

There are two fundamental types of dam, which have different ways of withstanding the pressure of water in the reservoir behind them: **gravity dams** and **wall dams**. The gravity dam depends on its own weight to prevent deformation or movement, whereas the wall dam is a rigid structure that resists deformation and transfers the pressure of the water to the floor and sides of the valley. Some dams are a combination of both types.

The simplest form of gravity dam is made up of carefully selected unconsolidated material such as clay or broken rock. This is called an *earth dam* (although it is not made of garden-type earth!). Earth dams usually have an impermeable clay core to reduce the seepage of water through the dam, and the sides are usually covered with broken blocks of rock or concrete to reduce erosion by waves. Gravity dams can also be constructed entirely of piled-up masonry (stone blocks) or concrete. *Masonry* or *concrete gravity dams* are usually built if the reservoir site is a narrow valley, but if a reservoir has to be built in a wide valley or in a lowland area, earth dams are used as they are less expensive. Figure 4.18 shows how the Aswan High Dam, an earth dam, was built. The Kielder Dam is also an earth dam (Figure 4.17).

Wall dams are usually built only in narrow valleys, when a relatively high dam is needed. They must be strong and impermeable, and are made of masonry or concrete. Their strength is often increased by making them curved in plan (convex towards the reservoir, just as curved arches are used to support heavy roofs in churches), or with buttresses on the downriver side (similar to those used to stop church walls falling outwards), or by reinforcing them internally with steel cables. The Hoover Dam on the Colorado River is an example of a wall dam (Figure 4.13).

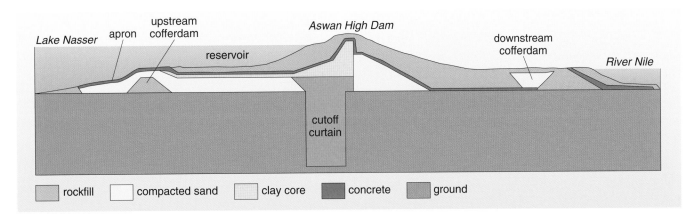

rockfill | compacted sand | clay core | concrete | ground

Figure 4.18   The Aswan High Dam on the River Nile, Egypt, shown in cross-section. This rock-filled gravity dam is 1.2 km long from side to side. It incorporates an upstream cofferdam and a downstream cofferdam. The cutoff curtain extends to a depth equal to one-and-a-half times the height of the central dam ridge. The water levels shown are the highest expected.

Seepage below dams can be reduced by a **cutoff curtain** and/or an **apron**. A cutoff curtain is a narrow impermeable layer, usually made of concrete, extending vertically below the dam, to reduce horizontal seepage of water under the dam (Figures 4.18 and 4.19a). The cutoff curtain extends downwards to a depth that is usually greater than the height of the dam, and if possible goes down into impermeable rock. An apron is a horizontal impermeable layer at the foot of the dam wall to reduce downward seepage from the reservoir (Figure 4.19b).

One of the problems of building a dam in the valley of a major river lies in excluding water from the dam site while the dam is being built. Small temporary dams, called **cofferdams**, are often constructed for this purpose, and are sometimes incorporated into the main dam (Figure 4.18).

4.3.3   Environmental effects of reservoir construction

Reservoirs may totally alter the water resources of a country. Before the Aswan Dam was completed in Egypt, more than half of the 8×10^{10} m^3 of water that flowed down the River Nile through Egypt each year ran into the sea. Most of the water can now be used in Egypt, mainly for irrigation, and instead of a single annual crop grown after seasonal flooding, more than one crop can be grown each year. However, advantages such as these must be considered in conjunction with the environmental side-effects of reservoir construction. The major side-effects are detailed below.

Land use

By their very nature, reservoirs occupy large areas of land. Lake Nasser, the reservoir created by the Aswan Dam, has an area of 6000 km^2, and even in Britain some 250 km^2 of land is covered by reservoirs. The largest in the UK is Kielder Water in Northumberland, which covers about 10.5 km^2. British reservoirs are generally in upland areas of scenic beauty that are otherwise suitable only for hiking and related pastimes, and as rough grazing for sheep, but reservoirs may cover up rich farmland or villages, or destroy sites of outstanding natural beauty or of archaeological importance. Land itself is an important resource, and drowning it under a reservoir may not be the best use of that resource, especially if the water can be supplied by alternative means.

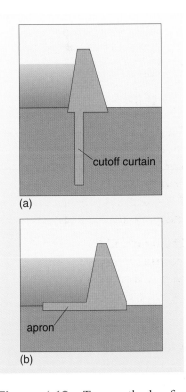

Figure 4.19   Two methods of reducing seepage under dams. (a) A cutoff curtain — an impervious wall in the foundation. (b) An apron — an impervious layer laid horizontally in front of the upstream face.

Ecological changes

Creation of a reservoir produces ecological changes not only to the area of the reservoir itself, by destroying the natural vegetation, but also upstream and downstream of the reservoir. The gradient of a river upstream of a reservoir may be reduced, so the water will slow down, changing the character of the river, causing deposition of sediment, and changes to the natural vegetation and animal life. Downstream of the reservoir the discharge will change, as well as the sediment load, also affecting the plants and animals. For example, annual flooding may cease.

Dam failure

Dams may collapse, releasing large amounts of water downstream, causing destruction of buildings and killing people and animals. Collapse may be caused by inappropriate construction, failure of the underlying sediments or rock, overfilling or earthquakes. The dam for the Carsington reservoir, in Derbyshire, collapsed during construction in 1984 due to failure of underlying sediments. Earthquake damage to dams is rare but does occur. Although China, for example, has thousands of dams in earthquake areas, none has collapsed in recent years from earthquake damage, but in the UK, an area of low earthquake activity, the Earl's Burn Dam near Stirling failed following an earthquake in 1839.

Sediment filling

The lifetime of reservoirs can vary greatly. Many reservoirs have lasted for over a hundred years, but some may be useful for only a much shorter period — fifty years or so — not because of the general deterioration of the dam as it gets older, but because sediment accumulates in the reservoir. Rivers carry large amounts of mud, silt and sand in suspension, particularly during floods, and when a river enters a reservoir it slows down and the sediment carried in suspension is deposited on the floor of the reservoir. Lake Mead, on the Colorado River, has had its storage capacity reduced by over a half since the dam was completed in 1935. This is less of a problem for UK reservoirs, as rivers here are smaller and carry much less sediment. The Derwent Valley reservoirs in Derbyshire have had their volumes reduced by less than 1% through sedimentation in the 70 years since they were completed. Some water-supply reservoirs are constructed so that sediment-laden floodwaters can bypass the reservoir, but obviously this is not possible where the reservoirs are intended for flood control.

Sediment loss to agriculture

The trapping of sediment behind dams may also affect agriculture. The Nile Valley, for example, used to flood naturally once a year, and the sediment in the waters was deposited on the land, forming a fertile soil. These floodwaters and the sediment they carry are now trapped behind the Aswan Dam, and artificial fertilizers must be used down river in the valley. Without the yearly supply of sediment in floodwater, the banks of the Nile are eroding downstream of the dam, and the Nile delta is reducing in size; the erosion by wave action no longer being counteracted by a fresh supply of sediment.

Soil salinization

The change from annual flooding by a river to perennial irrigation that can be provided from a reservoir can cause soil salinization, if salts normally present in the river water accumulate in the soil as the water evaporates. These salts were previously washed away by the flooding, but the reduced supply of water by irrigation leaves them in the soil. The water is taken in by plants, or evaporated by the sun, leaving the salts behind. This causes a decline in crop yields until eventually the soil becomes useless for agriculture. It can be prevented by using enough irrigation water to wash the salts through the soil, and draining this water from the fields.

Induced earthquakes

Some reservoirs *cause* earthquakes to occur. This is perhaps not so surprising, as earthquakes are caused by stress in rocks, and the addition of a large mass of water in a reservoir on top of the rocks at the Earth's surface stresses the rocks and can trigger an earthquake. Not all reservoirs induce earthquakes: it is in general only the larger reservoirs, or the deeper ones (over 100 m deep), and only if the reservoir is built in an earthquake area, releasing stress already stored in the rocks. Induced earthquakes mainly occur during *changes* in water level in a reservoir, particularly during initial filling or during seasonal changes of water level.

Reservoirs that have experienced induced earthquakes include Marathon, Greece (1931), Lake Mead, USA (from 1938), Kariba, Zimbabwe (1963), Lake Nasser, Egypt (from 1965), Koyna, India (1967) and Thomson, Australia (1996). So far (2004), none of these induced earthquakes have caused total dam failure, but the largest, at Koyna, was of considerable size (Richter magnitude 6.5, the equivalent of 100 Hiroshima atomic bombs), and led to damage of the dam.

Many of these environmental effects are illustrated by the Narmada Project (Box 4.4).

Box 4.4   The Narmada Valley Development Project, India: salvation or environmental disaster?

India suffers from widespread water scarcity, mainly because precipitation comes in one seasonal period, the monsoon, which lasts from about June to September (Figure 4.20). Reservoirs can be used to store the seasonal rain so it can be used year-round or transferred to an area of need. The Narmada River (the name means 'one who endows with bliss') is 1400 km long and is one of India's most sacred rivers. It originates in the centre of India and flows westwards through three states – Madhya Pradesh, Gujarat and Maharastra — and then into the Arabian Sea. These three states are particularly prone to prolonged drought.

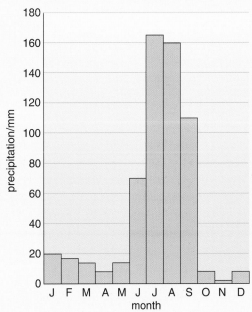

Figure 4.20   Average monthly precipitation values for New Delhi, India.

A project is under way (the Narmada Valley Development Project, NVDP) to build 30 major dams, along with smaller ones, on the river over the next 50 years, to supply drinking water for the region, for irrigation, to protect the area from flooding and to generate hydroelectric power. Its estimated cost is around $11 400 million, the most expensive construction project undertaken in India. In 1987, work began on the largest dam for the NVDP, Sardar Sarovar. The NVDP, and particularly the building of the giant dam, has caused huge controversy, both in India (Figure 4.21) and globally. The Sardar Sarovar dam has a planned final height of 139 m and the reservoir length is 214 km. It will displace around half a million people, and destroy forest as well as some of India's most fertile agricultural land.

Figure 4.21   Demonstrators against the construction of the Sardar Sarovar dam outside the United Nations building in New Delhi in 2000.

The main Indian opposition organization to the NVDP, the Narmarda Bachao Andolan (NBA), campaigned strongly against the dam, gaining support from both Indian and world opposition. In the 1980s NBA mobilized the local population, with marches, sit-ins and fasts (resulting in imprisonment for the leaders); caused the World Bank to review its funding of the project and to withdraw funding in 1993; and petitioned the Indian supreme court in 1994, which halted construction in 1995. However, in 2000 the supreme court ruled that the construction should go ahead, and at the time of writing (2004) the dam was near completion.

The scheme is enormously popular with the dam contractors and with political parties in those local Indian states which will benefit from the extra water and electricity. It is also popular with those who have had to walk miles to collect water each day and who do not have enough water to irrigate their crops. It is not popular, however, with those forced to move from villages that will be submerged, or environmental organizations that fear for the ecology of the Narmada.

Opposition to the NVDP is on social, environmental, economic and safety grounds:

- *Social*: huge numbers of people are evicted from their lands, homes, and traditional way of life, to make way for reservoirs. Past resettlement schemes in India have had a very poor record, offering poor land and a reduced standard of living.

- *Environmental*: the loss of agricultural land and forests, the loss of fisheries, contamination of water, a reduction in fertility of the land, and an increase in waterborne diseases.

- *Economic*: the water will be very expensive. Independent analyses by the World Bank, the Central Government of India and the NBA all find that the costs have been underestimated (and the benefits exaggerated).

- *Safety*: the Narmada valley is an earthquake area and has had substantial earthquakes in the past, up to magnitude 6.25. The Sardar Sarovar dam has also been built on a geological fault that may move in an earthquake. Any failure of the dam through an earthquake, unsound foundations, poor construction, failure of an upstream dam or terrorism could wipe out towns and villages downstream, killing hundreds of thousands of people.

The opponents' case is that the same benefits could be gained by a less grandiose scheme of local water projects, which could do the same job at a fraction of the cost, and with minimal environmental damage. This would involve decentralized, small rainwater harvesting schemes, more equitable sharing of water, water conservation, improved efficiency of water supply and irrigation, the restoration of degraded watershed vegetation and less water-intensive farming.

4.3.4   Big dams in the future?

Throughout the 20th century, reservoir construction to improve water resources was considered a key component of development. It was undertaken universally by industrialized nations, and by the later 20th century, increasingly by developing nations, building bigger and bigger dams. More recently the debate over the environmental impact of big dams and their questionable cost-benefit analysis has been universally recognized. In the 1990s the Narmada scheme caused the World Bank to rethink its policy on financing big dams, and also triggered the formation of the World Commission on Dams in 1998 which published the influential *Dams and Development: A New Framework for Decision-Making*, in 2000.

There is the question of **sustainable development** (summarized in Sheldon, 2005). To be sustainable, development must meet the needs of the present without compromising the ability of future generations to meet their own needs. Environmentalist opponents to the Narmada scheme argued that it is non-sustainable, given the environmental side-effects and the fear that the necessary maintenance of the dams, reservoirs and irrigation canals may not be carried out.

Many big dam projects are complicated by their multipurpose nature, for any combination of water supply, flood prevention, and hydroelectric power. These purposes may conflict, as we saw, for example, for the Hoover Dam in the USA. For Narmada, one of the opponents of the scheme, the Booker prize-winning Indian novelist Arundhati Roy, wrote:

> The thing about multipurpose dams like the Sardar Sarovar is that their purposes (irrigation, power production, and flood control) conflict with one another. Irrigation uses up the water you need to produce power. Flood control requires you to keep the reservoir empty during the monsoon months to deal with an anticipated surfeit of water. And if there's no surfeit, you're left with an empty dam. And this defeats the purpose of irrigation, which is to store the monsoon water.
>
> (Roy, 1999)

Will sustainable development mean that no new big dams are built for water resources in the 21st century?

4.4   Summary of Chapter 4

1   Many rivers are fed by springs, which occur at points where groundwater reaches the surface. Springs can occur in different geological settings, forming valley springs, stratum springs or solution channel springs.

2   The water in a river originates from overland flow, from interflow and from baseflow. Baseflow forms a higher proportion of river water in summer than in winter, and in rivers flowing over good aquifers.

3   River discharge at a particular point is usually determined by measuring the stage, which is the water level in the river, and then reading off a value for the discharge from the rating curve — a plot of measured discharge for various stages. A river discharge hydrograph is a record of the discharge

over a period of time. The shape of a short-period hydrograph (the record for a few days) depends on the size, shape, geology, vegetation and land use of the river catchment. The shape of the long-period hydrograph (e.g. for a year) depends primarily on the type of climate in the river catchment.

4   Reservoirs increase the amount of water stored on the land surface. They can be used as direct supply reservoirs or for river regulation. Reservoirs may also be built solely or partly for other purposes, such as the generation of hydroelectricity or for flood prevention.

5   The criteria for selecting sites for water-supply reservoirs are: a good supply of high-quality water, minimum ecological and environmental disturbance, a high elevation, a watertight reservoir area, no geological hazards and a suitable dam site. The most suitable reservoir sites are narrow, deep valleys, but reservoirs often have to be built in wider valleys or in flatter lowland areas.

6   There are two types of dams, gravity dams and wall dams. The gravity dam depends on its own weight to maintain stability, whereas the wall dam is a rigid structure that transfers the pressure of the water to the floor and sides of a valley.

7   The environmental effects of constructing a reservoir include the loss of a large area of land, ecological changes, dam failure, sediment filling, sediment loss to agriculture, soil salinization and induced earthquakes.

8   Reservoir projects involving big dams are becoming increasingly subject to scrutiny, particularly on the grounds of sustainable development.

WATER QUALITY

5.1 Natural waters

To judge what constitutes poor quality or polluted water, we must first understand the properties of naturally occurring waters. Natural water is not just H_2O: all natural waters contain dissolved and suspended substances — seawater is an obvious example of water containing dissolved salts, but freshwater does also, although at a far lower concentrations. Water **pollution** is defined as a *change in the quality of the water due to human activity that makes the water less suitable for use than it was originally* (Figure 5.1). It is difficult to set absolute standards of purity that apply for all uses of water however, because water that is considered clean enough for one purpose may be too polluted for another.

Figure 5.1 Faulty oil tanks leak oil into a river in New Orleans, USA. Because oil floats on water without dissolving, a small amount can quickly spread out to cover a large area. Some types of oil contain toxic compounds that can enter the food chain.

Rainwater, seawater and river water (Figure 5.2) and groundwaters (Figure 5.3) generally have very different chemical compositions and differ widely in their concentrations of **total dissolved solids (TDS)**. Average TDS values are: 7 mg l^{-1} for rainwater, 118 mg l^{-1} for river water and 34 400 mg l^{-1} for seawater. TDS values for groundwater vary too much for an average to be meaningful. TDS is a good indicator of water quality, and standards that have been set for drinking water and for water used in other ways include maximum values for TDS (Section 5.4).

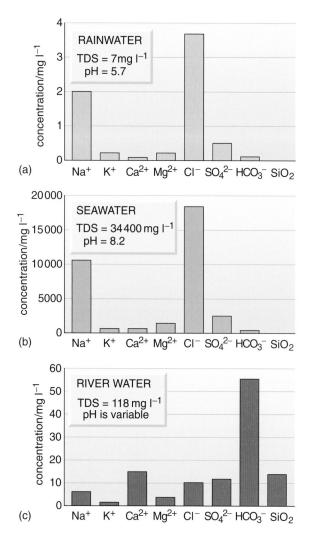

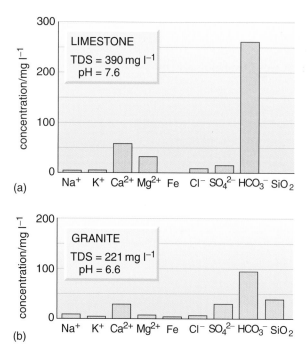

Figure 5.2 The average chemical compositions of (a) rainwater, (b) seawater and (c) river water. Only the major dissolved constituents are shown, and dissolved gases are not included. Different scales are used for each histogram. River water may vary considerably from the composition shown.

Figure 5.3 The chemical compositions of groundwaters from (a) limestone and (b) granite. (Fe includes both the Fe^{2+} and Fe^{3+} ions.)

Rainwater and seawater (Figure 5.2a and b) have similar *relative proportions* of dissolved solids, although rainwater is much more dilute. Most of the dissolved salts in rainwater come from sea spray dispersed into the atmosphere. A major difference in composition is the greater relative proportions of dissolved gases in rainwater, particularly carbon dioxide. Natural rainwater is slightly acidic as a result of this reaction, with an average pH of 5.7, whereas the average pH of seawater is 8.2 (Box 5.1). Rainwater may be even more acidic in areas where the highly soluble acidic gases sulphur dioxide and nitrogen dioxide (both produced by fossil fuel power generation, transportation and industrial processes) are present in the atmosphere.

Box 5.1 pH

pH is a measure of how acidic or alkaline a solution is. The pH scale ranges from less than 1 to 14, with low values the most acid, and high values the most alkaline. A neutral solution (or pure water) has a pH value of 7.

An acidic solution has a higher concentration of hydrogen ions, H^+, than pure water (this is where the 'H' in the term 'pH' comes from) and a pH of less than 7. For example, when carbon dioxide (CO_2) dissolves in water, a slightly acidic solution is formed:

$$H_2O + CO_2 = H^+ + HCO_3^-$$
$$\text{bicarbonate}$$

The pH of most natural waters lies between 5.5 and 8.5.

River water and groundwater differ from rainwater in that both have greater TDS values and different relative proportions of dissolved substances (Figures 5.2c and 5.3). Rivers may also contain solid particles in suspension, in addition to dissolved substances. Groundwater usually has a low content of suspended solids because these are filtered out as the water passes through the ground. Organic processes in soils, the solution of soluble minerals in rocks, interaction with clays and other minerals, and the chemical weathering of rocks are responsible for the changes in composition as rainwater becomes surface water or groundwater. The relative proportions of the dissolved substances change and the TDS value increases as a result of these processes. In general, groundwater takes on the chemical properties of the rocks through which it passes.

● What are the three principal dissolved constituents of river water and both groundwaters in Figures 5.2c and 5.3?

● For the river water and granitic groundwater the three most abundant are bicarbonate (HCO_3^-), calcium (Ca^{2+}) and silica (SiO_2). For the limestone groundwater, bicarbonate and calcium are again abundant, but magnesium (Mg^{2+}) is more abundant than silica (although this may not be the case for all limestones).

The main reason for the abundance of HCO_3^- and Ca^{2+} is the solution of calcium carbonate ($CaCO_3$) which can be present as limestone or as a cement in sandstone. Limestone is a fairly common rock, and it dissolves readily in acidic waters such as rainwater:

$$CaCO_3 + H^+ = Ca^{2+} + HCO_3^-$$

The mineral dolomite ($CaMg(CO_3)_2$) has a similar reaction in acidic water, and provides a source of magnesium ions. Magnesium also comes from the weathering of minerals such as olivine and pyroxene. Silica comes from the weathering of silicate minerals, which are a major constituent of most common rocks.

Box 5.2 Hardness in water

Hardness in water is mainly due to the presence of ions of the elements calcium, magnesium and iron. High concentrations of these ions have objectionable side-effects, particularly scum and scaling. The ions react with soap, forming insoluble compounds and preventing the soap from lathering properly, causing rings on bathtubs and leaving a grey soap scum on washed clothes. Hard water also leaves mineral deposits (limescale) in plumbing and appliances that use water, particularly kettles.

If the hard water contains bicarbonate ions, carbonate salts of the metals are precipitated when the water is boiled or heated above 70 °C. Such water is said to possess *temporary hardness* because the carbonate salts are largely insoluble and are thus removed from the water as limescale deposits.

$$Ca^{2+} + 2HCO_3^- = H_2O + CO_2 + CaCO_3$$
calcium carbonate
(limescale)

When the main anions (negatively charged ions) present are chloride, sulphate or nitrate, the hardness is called *permanent hardness*, which cannot be removed by boiling.

Some people in hard water areas use water softeners, which usually replace calcium, magnesium, and certain other ions in the water with sodium ions. The sodium ions are supplied from common salt (sodium chloride) in the water softener. While softened water containing sodium ions in moderate concentration is unobjectionable in taste or household use, it may be of concern to those who, for health reasons, are on diets involving restricted sodium intake.

In spite of the problems encountered when boiling and using soap in hard water, the dissolved solids may give hard water a pleasant taste and have various medicinal benefits.

The extent of hard water in Britain tends to follow a north to south-east gradient; the softest water is in Scotland, northern England and Wales, and the hardest is in East Anglia and south-east England. Death from cardiovascular (CV) disease (heart disease and stroke) tends to follow a similar pattern — a higher rate in the north and north-west than the south and the south-east. Several statistical surveys in a number of other countries have also shown this inverse relationship between CV disease and water hardness, i.e. CV disease is more common in softer-water areas. However, there is no evidence of a direct causative link between CV disease and soft water, but as a precaution standards have been set for water that has been artificially softened. The UK has set restrictions on levels of water softening, and UK drinking water should now have a minimum hardness, *if* it has been softened, of 60 mg l^{-1} of Ca^{2+}.

The composition of water will vary with the type of rock the water has flowed over or through. Water flowing through igneous and metamorphic rocks usually has lower TDS values than that flowing through sedimentary rocks, because igneous and metamorphic rocks contain minerals that are generally less soluble. Water that has flowed through deposits of ore minerals will often have a high metal ion content and may have a high sulphate content, derived from sulphide ore minerals.

The TDS value of the water also depends on the length of time the water has been in contact with rock. Groundwaters usually have higher TDS values because the residence time of groundwater is generally higher than that of surface water (Table 2.1, Section 2.1). The composition of groundwater changes as it passes through an aquifer. Near the recharge area, groundwater has low TDS values, but as the water flows through the aquifer it gains more dissolved substances, so the TDS values are usually higher at discharge points.

In hot dry regions where rainfall is low and evaporation is high, there is little infiltration and the soluble products of chemical weathering are flushed from aquifers very slowly. So groundwaters can have high TDS values in these areas.

Deeper groundwaters that are slow moving often have particularly high concentrations of dissolved substances with TDS values exceeding a few thousand milligrams per litre. Sodium chloride is usually a major constituent of these waters. When these saline waters are discharged at the surface they are often called **mineral waters** (Figure 5.4).

Figure 5.4   In Bath, UK, hot mineral water at a temperature of 46 °C rises at the rate of around a million litres every day and has been doing this for thousands of years. The mineral water was used in the Roman Baths, one of the best-preserved Roman sites north of the Alps.

Looking back at Figure 5.3, why does the groundwater from the limestone area have a higher TDS value than the groundwater from the granite area?

Minerals in the limestone are much more soluble than the minerals in granite, especially if the water is slightly acidic. The high TDS is caused mainly by calcium and bicarbonate ions.

The variation in natural waters may make it hard to determine when water is polluted. Although pollution means a deterioration in water quality caused by human agencies, the same *effect* may occur naturally. For instance, large amounts of sediment and vegetable matter can be washed into rivers during rainstorms; toxic metals and acid waters can get into rivers and groundwaters where concentrations of ore minerals occur; and contamination can result from oil seepages at the surface. These are all natural processes, and many of the effects will be neutralized in time; the environment has ways of adapting itself in the long term. Pollution, on the other hand, can be on a very large scale, can happen rapidly, can take a variety of forms, and can upset the ecological balance where it occurs.

5.2   Pollutants

We shall now look at the most common water pollutants, their sources, their effects, and how they can be controlled. A summary is provided in Table 5.1 and some points are discussed below in more detail.

Table 5.1   The nature, sources, effects and control of some major types of pollutants.

Pollutant	Nature	Common sources	Effects of pollution	Control
natural organic material	biodegradable organic materials; normally decomposed by aerobic bacteria (which require water-dissolved oxygen)	domestic sewage; food-processing industries; farms	excessive depletion of oxygen in water damages aquatic life; complete removal of oxygen causes anaerobic bacterial action on pollutants, resulting in offensive smells	sewage treatment works, by physical and biological processes; containment of sewage, cattle slurry and silage effluent
living organisms	disease-causing organisms (bacteria, viruses)	human and animal wastes; certain industries (e.g. tanning, slaughtering)	curtailed recreational use of rivers, lakes, etc.	most commonly controlled with chlorine; seldom possible to remove all bacterial and viral contamination, but concentrations are greatly reduced
plant nutrients	principally nitrogen and phosphorus compounds	domestic sewage; industrial wastes; farms (especially from chemical fertilizers)	excessive growth of aquatic plant life leads to oxygen depletion, offensive smells, bad taste; excess nitrate in drinking water could be toxic	serious problem: not removed by ordinary sewage treatment methods; very expensive to reduce
organic chemicals	detergents, herbicides, pesticides, industrial by-products, medicines	domestic sewage and industrial waste; farms	poison — threat to fish and other wildlife; possible long-term hazards to human beings	very often not removed by usual sewage or water purification treatments
inorganic chemicals	salt, acids, metallic salts, cyanides, etc.	mining; industrial processes; natural deposits (e.g. salt); road salting in winter	toxic effects on humans and wildlife; interference with manufacturing processes; bad smells and tastes; corrosion of equipment	difficult: non-standard processes necessary
sediments	primarily soils and minerals; also some industrial by-products	land erosion by storms; flood waters; some industrial, quarrying and mining processes	obstruction or filling of rivers, lakes, reservoirs; increased cost of water purification; interference with manufacturing processes; equipment corrosion; reduced aquatic life and diversity	controlled by use of soil conservation and flood control methods; also by improvement of industrial technology; reduced by settling ponds
heat	heated water returned to rivers and lakes	electric power plants; steel mills; refineries and other industrial cooling units	reduction of oxygen in the water, resulting in slower or incomplete pollutant decomposition and harm to aquatic life	minimized by recirculation and reuse of industrial cooling waters

5.2.1 Natural organic material

Much of the natural organic material found as a pollutant in water comes from domestic sewage and the effluents of farms and food-processing industries. Farm waste can be especially polluting and is an important EU issue: cattle slurry is up to 100 times as polluting per cubic metre as domestic sewage, and silage effluent is up to 200 times as polluting (Figure 5.5). Natural organic material consists of carbohydrates, proteins and fats, plus a number of other substances in lesser amounts. These are **biodegradable**; that is, they can be broken down by bacteria and other organisms into relatively harmless end-products. If sufficient oxygen is present in the water, aerobic bacteria (oxygen-using bacteria) feed on the organic material, using oxygen dissolved in the water. The polluting material is converted into water, carbon dioxide (CO_2), nitrates (NO_3^-), sulphates (SO_4^{2-}) and phosphates (PO_4^{3-}). This process can continue as long as the bacteria can get enough oxygen from the water.

Figure 5.5   Silage, made by fermenting grass, is useful for feeding farm animals in winter. Effluent produced by the silage-making process is highly polluting.

The oxygen concentration of unpolluted fresh water is around $10 \, \text{mg l}^{-1}$. The actual concentration depends partly on the rate at which oxygen is supplied by aquatic plants through photosynthesis and partly on the rate at which it is dissolved from the air — more oxygen is dissolved where there is a proportionately large surface area of water in contact with the air, such as in shallow ponds or turbulent rivers. Another important influence on oxygen concentration is temperature. The higher the temperature, the lower the amount of dissolved oxygen in the water: at $10 \, ^\circ\text{C}$ the concentration is about $11 \, \text{mg l}^{-1}$, falling to about $9 \, \text{mg l}^{-1}$ at $20 \, ^\circ\text{C}$.

If excessive amounts of natural organic materials are discharged into a body of water, the demands of the bacteria feeding on it exceed the rate at which the oxygen can be replenished, and the oxygen concentration falls. This brings about a reduction in aquatic life; many animals in the water will die as the oxygen concentration decreases, and few plants thrive when organic pollution is severe. Trout and salmon die when the oxygen concentration falls below $3 \, \text{mg l}^{-1}$, and aerobic bacteria will not survive at concentrations below about $0.5 \, \text{mg l}^{-1}$.

At this point the decomposition of the polluting organic material is taken over by anaerobic bacteria (bacteria that exist in the absence of oxygen). These bacteria reduce the organic material to a different set of end-products — hydrogen sulphide (H_2S), ammonia (NH_3) and methane (CH_4). They give the water a foul smell and indicate severe pollution.

The **biochemical oxygen demand (BOD)** is a measure of how much natural organic material — sewage, sewage effluent or industrial effluent — is present in a body of water. BOD is defined as the amount of oxygen taken up by micro-organisms (principally bacteria) in decomposing the organic material in a water sample stored in darkness for 5 days at $20 \, ^\circ\text{C}$. Water with a high BOD has a low level of dissolved oxygen.

Rivers have some capacity for self-purification after pollution by biodegradable, natural organic materials. Figure 5.6 shows the effects of pollution downstream from a sewage outfall on one particular river.

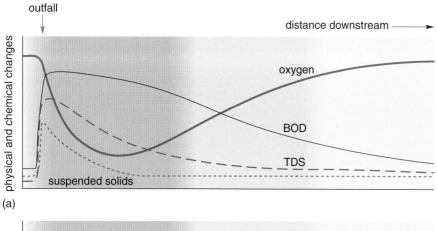

(a)

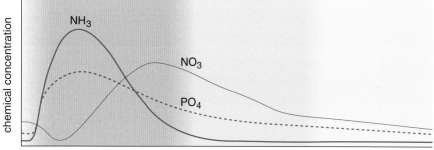

(b)

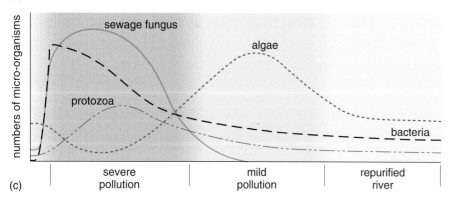

(c)

Figure 5.6 Typical changes in a river downstream of a sewage outfall.

Question 5.1

(a) Downstream from the sewage outfall, the dissolved oxygen in the water rapidly decreases and then gradually increases again (Figure 5.6a). How can this be explained?

(b) How do the concentrations of ammonia (NH_3) in Figure 5.6b vary?

(c) Which organisms appear to be most able to tolerate the pollution (Figure 5.6c)?

(d) What is the most likely explanation for the changes in the distribution of the organisms downstream of the sewage outfall?

5.2.2   Living organisms

Besides the living organisms that form part of the natural cycle in rivers, there are other organisms that are less desirable. Their presence is generally due to human activities, and they are a form of pollution. Many of these organisms are **pathogenic bacteria**, which can cause disease. The most common source of pathogenic bacteria is sewage, and the purpose of the 19th century legislation in England and Wales prohibiting the discharge of raw sewage into rivers was to prevent the spread of disease. Pathogenic bacteria are adapted to body temperatures so they die off relatively quickly in cold river waters. For example, typhoid bacteria die within seven days in river water at the temperatures found in Britain — but a week is long enough to spread infection.

As well as bacteria, there are other aquatic organisms that may be harmful. Diseases may also be transmitted by protozoa, worms, snails and insect larvae (Figure 5.7).

Non-pathogenic bacteria are also part of the aquatic system. One such bacterium, *Escherichia coli* (*E. coli*), has various strains, most of which are non-pathogenic and exist in human and animal intestines in a symbiotic relationship, making substances needed by humans and animals. The presence of *E. coli* in river water is therefore a useful indication of faecal pollution. The **coliform count** (the number of coliform bacteria, of which *E. coli* is one, present in a fixed volume of water) is used as a measure of the extent of such pollution.

Figure 5.7   Mosquito larvae hanging under a water surface. The adult mosquito hatches after a period of pupation and can transmit diseases such as malaria.

5.2.3   Plant nutrients

Plant nutrients are inorganic substances — mainly nitrogen and phosphorus compounds — that are essential for normal plant growth. Nitrogen and phosphorus come from human and animal faeces, detergents and fertilizers, and are not removed by standard water treatment processes or by sewage treatment. If the concentration of these nutrients in water gets too high they can cause a rapid proliferation of algae — an algal bloom (Figure 5.8). This can discolour the water, give it a bad taste and smell, and may produce a green scum on the surface. When they die, the algae sink and decay, forming large amounts of natural organic material with a high oxygen demand. The water becomes deoxygenated and polluted even further. This type of pollution is not usually a problem in British rivers but it does affect some reservoirs, lakes and canals.

Figure 5.8   An algal bloom in a stream caused by fertilizer runoff from farmland.

5.2.4   Organic and inorganic chemicals

Organic and inorganic chemicals can become pollutants when they are washed into rivers, lakes or the sea. Some of the chemicals are toxic, depending on their concentrations. Toxic organic substances include agricultural pesticides such as dichlorodiphenyltrichloroethane (DDT) and dimethyl mercury and also polychlorinated biphenyls (PCBs), which are by-products of the plastics industry. DDT and PCBs are particularly dangerous as they are very stable and not biodegradable, so they can accumulate in water and in living organisms. Because of this, the use of DDT is now banned in most industrialized countries, although it is still used in most developing ones as it is a cheap and effective pesticide. Toxic inorganic substances include salts of the metals copper, silver, lead, gold, nickel, chromium, zinc, cadmium and mercury, and the metalloid arsenic. Many of these are toxic even at low concentrations: less than 1 mg l^{-1}. Most are wastes from industrial processes or mining (Figure 5.9).

Figure 5.9   Acid mine drainage in the Carnon River, Cornwall from the Wheal Jane mine, an example of inorganic chemical pollution caused by oxidation of sulphide minerals. The water and sediment is coloured orange by compounds of iron and other metals.

5.2.5   Heat

Heat has two main effects. As mentioned when discussing natural organic pollutants, a rise in temperature brings about a decrease in the amount of oxygen dissolved in the water. At the same time, a rise in temperature increases the metabolic rate of organisms and therefore their demand for oxygen.

Heat can also cause fish to spawn and hatch out of season and to alter their migration patterns. To avoid such problems, when heated water is returned to rivers after being used for cooling (in power stations, for example), there should always be a minimum flow in the river to dissipate the heat sufficiently and so keep the temperature rise to only a few degrees.

5.3   The extent of water pollution

Water may become polluted by discharges (e.g. from sewage works or industry), overland flow (e.g. from farmland) or incidents (e.g. rupture of a farm slurry tank). We will start by looking at surface water pollution, then consider groundwater pollution.

5.3.1   Surface water

River water quality is important because rivers are a major source of water used for drinking and by industry. Rivers also support a wide variety of wildlife and in some areas of the world are used extensively for recreation. Chemical and biological quality is affected by the management of abstractions from rivers and groundwaters and how effluent returns to them, and by the design and maintenance of navigation and flood control measures.

In the UK, discharges into surface waters require the consent of the pollution control authority: the Environment Agency (EA) in England and Wales, the Scottish Environment Protection Agency (SEPA) in Scotland and the Environment and Heritage Service (EHS) of the Department of the Environment in Northern Ireland.

River water quality is one of the UK Government's 15 headline indicators of sustainable development. These are a 'quality of life barometer' measuring everyday concerns like housing development, health, jobs, air quality, educational achievement, wildlife and economic prosperity. They are intended to focus public attention on what sustainable development means and to give a broad overview of whether we are 'achieving a better quality of life for everyone, now and for generations to come' (DEFRA, 2002). River water quality is measured by indicators of chemical quality and biological quality. In England, Wales and Northern Ireland, three measurements are used for the chemical quality classification of river water: BOD, dissolved oxygen and ammonia. In Scotland, iron and pH are also included. Biological testing provides a more comprehensive picture of the health of rivers and canals, and is based on the monitoring of tiny animals which live in or on the bed of the river. Species groups recorded at a site are compared with those which would be expected to be present in the absence of pollution, allowing for different environmental characteristics in different parts of the country.

Table 5.2 gives chemical quality data for the rivers in the UK in 2002. Overall for the UK, it is estimated that about 95% of rivers were of good or fair chemical quality in 2002. These estimates are approximate because the classification scheme in Scotland differs from that in England, Wales and Northern Ireland. There has been an improvement in the proportion of rivers of good or fair quality in the UK since 1990 (Figure 5.10). This conclusion is based on a comparison of the trends for individual countries — an exact percentage change cannot be given because of changes both in monitoring methods and the monitored river networks through the period. Regional variations in England and Wales are illustrated in more detail in Figure 5.11.

Table 5.2 Chemical quality of river water in the UK, 2002.

| | % of classified river length | | | Total river lengths classified/km |
	Good	Fair	Poor/Bad	
England	65	28	6	36 170
Wales	92	6	2	4 570
Northern Ireland	55	42	4	4 130
Scotland	86	10	4	25 440

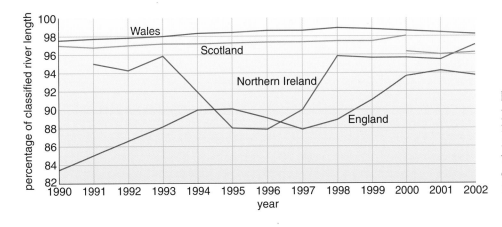

Figure 5.10 Variation in proportion of rivers of good or fair chemical quality (as in Table 5.2) 1990–2002. Monitoring of the Scottish river network changed in 2000. (Source: EA, SEPA, EHS.)

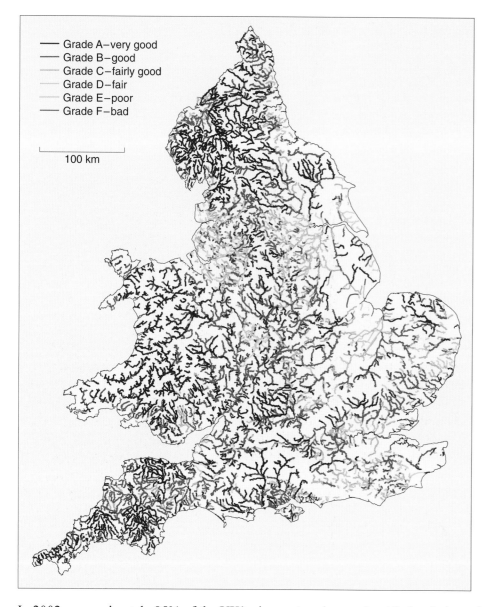

Grade A–very good
Grade B–good
Grade C–fairly good
Grade D–fair
Grade E–poor
Grade F–bad

100 km

Figure 5.11 Chemical quality of river water in England and Wales, 2002. The 'good' category in Table 5.2 is subdivided here into A, B and C.

In 2002, approximately 95% of the UK's river network was classified as being of good or fair biological quality (Table 5.3). Between 1990 and 2002, the biological quality of rivers improved in England. In Wales almost all rivers are of good or fair quality. The river length used for biological monitoring in Northern Ireland was more than doubled between 1995 and 2000 and there was a fall in river length of good quality. In Scotland biological quality is generally high, but changes in monitoring and network definitions mean it is difficult to draw conclusions about trends.

Table 5.3 Biological quality of river water in the UK, 2002.

	% of classified river length			Total river lengths classified/km
	Good	**Fair**	**Poor/Bad**	
England	68	27	5	33 500
Wales	78	21	1	4 380
Northern Ireland	57	40	3	5 140
Scotland	86	11	3	8 610

Although there has been a general improvement in river water quality in England and Wales between 1990 and 2002, before this, between 1980 and 1990, there was a general deterioration of water quality. This deterioration was caused by a combination of greater discharges from sewage works, industry and farms, overland flow from farmland, and two years of low rainfall and hot summers. In the south-west, intensive agriculture was the main cause, producing large quantities of animal slurry and silage effluent. Drought and pollution from sewage works were the main causes in the Thames area. In contrast, river quality surveys before 1980 showed a gradual improvement: the Thames is an appropriate example of this (Box 5.3).

Box 5.3 The River Thames: pollution, cleanup, pollution, cleanup

The River Thames in London has had a history of pollution problems. It has a low mean annual discharge ($82\,\text{m}^3\,\text{s}^{-1}$) in comparison with the London population of around 11 million.

Before the 19th century, domestic waste from London was collected in cesspools and used as a fertilizer on agricultural land (the origin of the term 'sewage farm'). Water closets began to be introduced in the mid-19th century, the waste flowing through sewers untreated to the Thames, and with the rise of industrial waste during the Industrial Revolution, which also flowed into the Thames, the river became highly polluted. The smell of the river was so bad that the Houses of Parliament (on the bank of the Thames) became a very unpleasant place to be and, in the best NIMBY ('not in my backyard') tradition, spurred Parliament to pass laws to control discharges to the river. London's sewage was piped downstream of the city where it was discharged, still untreated. This produced some improvement, and by the end of the 19th century the river quality began to improve (Figure 5.12). A good quality river will have an oxygen level close to 100% saturation — but if a river is polluted, oxygen in the water will be used in the breakdown of organic pollutants (Section 5.2) and the oxygen concentration will fall. The oxygen in the river in Figure 5.6, for example, was reduced to about a quarter just downstream of the sewage outfall.

However, by the mid-20th century, increasing population and industrialization, poor sewage treatment and sewer damage during the Second World War caused pollution of the river to increase, and oxygen was almost absent over a 60 km stretch of the River Thames by the 1950s (Figure 5.12). This part of the river contained water of very poor quality, and fish were absent. Since the 1950s, however, more extensive and improved treatment of sewage before the effluent is discharged to the river has improved the quality of the water.

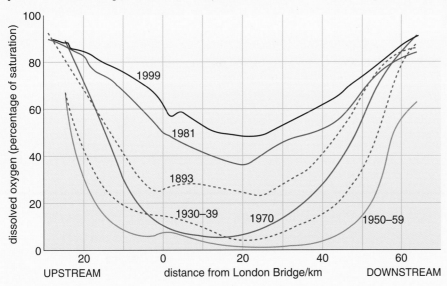

Figure 5.12 Dissolved oxygen in the River Thames between 1893 and 1999 for the months July to October, when discharge is low and pollution is greatest.

Question 5.2

From Figure 5.11, how does the chemical river quality of the river(s) where you live (or if you live outside England and Wales, at the location of the Open University, about 80 km north of London) compare with the average for England or Wales (Table 5.2)?

On an international scale, cleaning up polluted rivers or lakes is more complicated when they pass through more than one country. For example, the River Rhine has parts of its catchment in eight countries, and an almost total lack of pollution control has resulted in the Rhine being probably the most polluted large river in the world (Box 5.4).

Box 5.4   The River Rhine: attempts at international management of pollution

The headwaters of the River Rhine are in the Swiss Alps. It then flows through one of the most industrialized and densely populated areas of the world in Germany, France and the Netherlands. The Rhine river catchment area is 190 000 km². Until recently, countries have tended to dump waste into the River Rhine and then leave it to be dealt with by the next country downstream. There are 50 million inhabitants in the highly industrialized Rhine river basin, and their domestic and industrial wastes, often untreated, go into the river. Parts of the Rhine basin are intensively farmed, and fertilizers and agricultural chemicals also add to pollution in the river. The uses are often at odds with each other; for example, the Netherlands needs Rhine water for irrigation, but the high salinity of the Rhine, which can reach 600 mg l^{-1} at the Germany–Netherlands border, and comes mainly from French potash mines, can make the water unsuitable.

International agreements and cooperation have been necessary to reduce pollution of the river. At the insistence of the Netherlands, which was concerned about increased salinity, France, Germany, Luxembourg, the Netherlands, and Switzerland began discussing arrangements for reducing pollution in the 1950s, and formed the International Commission for the Protection of the Rhine against Pollution (IKSR) in 1953. This was a technical commission, charged with monitoring pollutants. To stem increasing pollution from industrial and municipal sources, the parties to the IKSR signed the Convention for the Protection of the Rhine against Chemical Pollution in 1976. In 1986 they agreed to the Rhine Action Programme, which seeks to produce drinkable water from the Rhine, reduce sediment pollution, and restore the Rhine environment so that aquatic life returns. The IKSR parties agreed to a 50% reduction (from 1985 levels) in the discharge of 30 priority pollutants into the river by 1995, and this was achieved. France, Germany, the Netherlands and Switzerland agreed to share costs of $136 million. In the summer of 1991, the German chemical industry federation agreed to reduce the discharge of toxic chemicals into the Rhine. These international efforts, combined with domestic pollution controls, particularly sewage treatment, have produced measurable benefits: since the early 1970s, concentrations of heavy metals have fallen and biological treatment of organic waste has reduced oxygen depletion and fish deaths.

There has been some success in reducing pollution; metal pollution has declined considerably, mainly due to better industrial sewage treatment. However, so far (2004), international agreements have failed to control some key pollutants; salt pollution is still a problem and desalination would be expensive. Nitrate concentrations, mainly because of heavy fertilizer use, continue to rise, and groundwater in Germany is increasingly contaminated with nitrate and pesticides. There is also the danger of accidental pollution. In 1986 a warehouse full of pesticides caught fire near Basel, Switzerland. The water used to control the fire washed 10 000 tonnes of toxic chemicals into the river, killing fish and other living organisms for several hundred kilometres downstream.

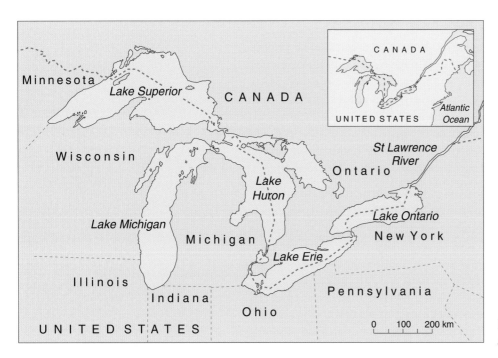

Figure 5.13 The North American Great Lakes.

The North American Great Lakes (Figure 5.13) also have major pollution problems. The Great Lakes are the world's largest freshwater ecosystem, with a catchment area of around 520 000 km^2. The lakes are interconnected, and have just one outlet to the sea, through the St Lawrence River to the Atlantic Ocean. They have many uses — as a large freshwater fishery, a source of water and hydroelectric power, transport by shipping (Figure 5.14), and recreation — and are surrounded by urban, agricultural and industrial development. This vast area falls under the control of eight US States and Canada.

The problems of the Great Lakes began with logging, which polluted the rivers with sawdust, followed by indiscriminate fishing, untreated sewage disposal which caused cholera and typhoid outbreaks in the early part of the 20th century, and lastly industrial waste disposal that was a particular problem from the 1950s. Lake Erie is bordered by five States, each of which dumped untreated sewage, acid, oil, iron and other industrial waste into the lake; by the 1960s the lake suffered from algal blooms and beaches were covered with rotting algae and dead fish. Many aquatic species became locally extinct and the fishing industry of Lake Erie was destroyed. This crisis provided an impetus for Canada and the USA to reduce sewage and industrial waste-water discharges into the lakes and rivers, but despite these stricter regulations pollution is still a problem. Only about 1% of the water in the system flows out to sea each year, so pollution of the water and in the bottom sediments tends to remain for a long time. Persistent organic chemicals and toxic metallic salts are the biggest problem.

Figure 5.14 Shipping on the Great Lakes.

5.3.2 Groundwater

Pollution is not restricted to surface waters; groundwater can also be polluted. Aquifers are vulnerable to contamination from human activities associated with agriculture, industry and waste disposal, and from chemical spills such as solvents and fuel oils. Pollution can either come from a point source, or from a widespread area of land (for example, agriculture). Once in an aquifer, groundwater pollution is difficult to clean up because it is not easily accessible, flow rates are low and residence times are long, so it may take a long time to disperse pollutants naturally and their effects may continue for a long time.

The only way to protect groundwater from pollution is, therefore, to prevent pollution happening. Protection zones can be established to reduce widespread pollution by restricting potentially polluting activities (as we shall see for nitrate in Section 5.4). Point discharges can also be controlled. Some of the potentially most polluting point sources are from landfills. Landfills are used to dispose of solid waste from domestic and industrial sources, and are used as they are often the cheapest method of disposal. Landfill waste can be a source of groundwater pollution as they produce **leachates**, liquids that form as water percolates through the waste, dissolving soluble compounds and the products of chemical and biochemical reactions that have taken place in the waste.

In the past, leachates were allowed to infiltrate into the ground below the landfill and into underlying aquifers where it was diluted by groundwater and gradually dispersed. However, this pollution of groundwater may lead to problems with the quality of groundwater used for water supply, and the practice is now regarded as unacceptable. To prevent the leachate from infiltrating into the ground below a landfill site, a landfill needs to be constructed so that the leachate is contained. The site can be lined with impermeable clay and/or a synthetic membrane, to prevent leachate escaping (Figure 5.15). The leachate is then collected and treated.

Figure 5.15 The installation of an impermeable liner and a leachate pump at a landfill site.

5.4 Treatment of water supplies

Water quality standards are necessary to ensure that supplies are suitable for use. The quality required depends on the intended use: drinking water, for example, needs quality standards different from those for industrial or irrigation water. The World Health Organization (WHO) has set guidelines for drinking water (1993), and so has the EU (1998) in Directive 98/83/EC (Table 5.4). The standards cover:

- bacteria
- chemicals such as metals, nitrate and pesticides
- the way water looks and how it tastes.

However, in many developing countries, which have a piped water supply only in some areas, there are no drinking water standards; water is often taken from the nearest river, and may be of very poor quality, leading to disease. A better source in these areas is pumped groundwater, as groundwater is often less polluted than surface water, but again there is no control on quality.

Table 5.4 EU Drinking Water Directive 98/83/EC: selected parameters and concentrations.

The full standards include many other substances not listed here. $1\,mg\,l^{-1} = 1000\,\mu g\,l^{-1}$; $1\,mg\,l^{-1} = 1\,ppm$.

	Concentration	
	Guide value/mg l^{-1}	Maximum acceptable/µg l^{-1}
aluminium	0.2	
ammonium	0.5	
arsenic		10
benzene		1
cadmium		5
calcium	250	
chloride	250	
copper	2	
cyanide		50
fluoride	1.5	
iron	0.2	
lead		25†
mercury		1
nitrate	50	
pesticides, individual		0.1
pesticides, total		0.5
sodium	200	
sulphate	250	
Other parameters		
pH range	6.5–9.5	
coliforms	none	
clostridium	none	

† lead after 2013 $= 10\,\mu g\,l^{-1}$.

Activity 5.1

This activity looks at the chemical composition of bottled drinking water. Bottled waters are often described on the label as mineral waters, a scientifically inappropriate term, as the scientific meaning of mineral water is high-TDS groundwater, which would not be suitable for drinking. Bottled water is perhaps surprisingly not subject to the general EU Drinking Water Directive, but has its own directive.

(a) Examine the label of any bottled water you have at home (or visit a shop to examine the label of such a bottle) and write down the dissolved substances it contains, with their concentrations (EU regulations require bottled waters to give this on their labels).

(b) Compare your list with the EU drinking water standards in Table 5.4. Does your bottled water exceed the EU guide values or maximum acceptable concentrations for any dissolved substance in drinking water?

The quality of the water required for industrial processes depends on the process so there is no general set of standards for industrial water equivalent to the standards for drinking water. High-pressure boilers require water of the highest quality, with more rigorous standards than for drinking water, whereas low-quality water, such as seawater, is usually adequate for cooling.

There are also no general standards for irrigation water; but there are three main quality criteria, as given below:

1   The maximum TDS of water that can be used for irrigation is usually 3000 mg l^{-1}, but this is not a precise limit, as different crops have different salt tolerances. Few fruit trees, for example, will tolerate much salt (2500 mg l^{-1} is usually the limit), vegetables and most cereals have a moderate salt tolerance (3500 mg l^{-1}), and grasses, cotton and date palms have a high tolerance (6000 mg l^{-1}).

2   Water with a higher sodium concentration than the combined calcium and magnesium concentrations is also generally unsuitable as it may damage the soil structure. The sodium ions can replace calcium and magnesium ions in the soil, which reduces the permeability, and the soil will be sticky when wet and very hard when dry.

3   Toxic substances, if present in more than very small quantities in irrigation water, will prevent plant growth. For example, a concentration of more than about 1 mg l^{-1} of the element boron will restrict growth.

5.4.1   Water treatment processes

The quality of public water supplies can be improved by water treatment, and this may be necessary before water from a particular source can be used. The most common treatment processes, in sequence, are:

- *Screening*   Debris such as leaves and plant fragments are removed by passing the water through a series of coarse metal screens.

- *Settling and oxidizing*   The water is then stored in a reservoir (or settling pond), so that sediments and some of the organic particles that escaped the straining process settle on the bottom, and the bacteria (which are all too small to be removed by straining) gradually die. Storage has the disadvantages that the reservoirs required use a lot of land, and algae may grow in the water because of a build-up of nitrates. Other organic impurities, which can give a taste or odour to the water, are oxidized in the upper layers of the reservoir. Water sprays, rather like fountains, are often used to aerate the water (Figure 5.16) so that the concentration of dissolved oxygen in the water is increased. Thus organic impurities can be oxidized to harmless substances, and some dissolved metal ions are oxidized to give insoluble compounds that can then be filtered out of the water.

- *Flocculation*   Even after straining and storage, raw water may contain considerable quantities of suspended matter. Most of this consists of colloidal matter (which is matter about 10^{-8} m in diameter in a form between solution and particulate form, and having negative electric charges).

Figure 5.16   A water spray can be used to aerate water in a settling pond, to increase the oxidation of organic impurities.

The colloidal matter can be reduced by filtration; but if there is a considerable quantity, it is usually more economic to make it *flocculate*. (The colloidal particles are neutralized by adding a chemical to the water that has the opposite charge to the colloidal particles. The particles then coalesce into bigger particles and sink out of the water.)

- *Filtration*   Filtration through sand and gravel then removes any fine particles of suspended matter and small organisms (mostly less than about 6×10^{-5} m in diameter) that still remain. In addition, algae and bacteria develop on and below the surface of the sand, where they decompose organic matter in the water passing through and digest some of the nitrates, phosphates and carbon dioxide dissolved in it, thus further purifying the water.

- *pH correction*   The EU guideline for the pH of drinking water is 6.5–9.5 (Table 5.4); this range was chosen because more acidic water might dissolve metal pipes in the distribution system and more alkaline water might leave salt deposits in the pipes. In the UK it is often necessary to add an alkali such as lime to water with a low pH, especially the water from peaty upland areas.

- *Disinfection*   The final treated water should contain no pathogenic bacteria, so the water must be disinfected. In the UK the most common method of disinfection is the use of chlorine (occasionally you may notice a slight smell of chlorine in your tap water). It is a method that has been used extensively for over 70 years. Water companies have to ensure that enough chlorine remains in the water after it leaves the treatment works to help keep the water safe on its journey to the tap. Other forms of disinfection include ozone and ultraviolet light, but these do not remain in the water during distribution, so in both cases a small amount of chlorine is added before the water goes into the distribution system. Disinfection is not very effective against parasites such as *Cryptosporidium* and *Giardia* (which can cause illnesses with severe diarrhoea lasting a number of weeks). If there is a risk of these being present they must be removed during the filtration stage of treatment.

Some waters require more specialized treatments which are expensive, such as:

- *Ion exchange*   This process is used to remove nitrate from groundwater (Box 5.5), and in some cases to soften water. Ion exchange is very similar to the process used in domestic water softeners, where water is passed through a bed of special resin particles.

- *Activated carbon*   Activated carbon, often in association with ozone, is used to remove organic substances. Some of these substances occur naturally and others are contaminants, such as pesticides, that occur because of human activities. The ozone breaks down the organic substances, which are then adsorbed on the surface of the carbon.

- *Softening*   Excessive hardness of water is usually reduced ('softened') by precipitation or by the exchange of ions brought about by adding appropriate chemicals.

Most developing countries, however, not only cannot afford to disinfect their water, but outside the main towns often have no piped water to disinfect. Every year, millions of people, particularly children, die of diarrhoea infections carried by contaminated water.

Box 5.5 Nitrate in drinking water

Intensive farming has caused the nitrate concentration in surface water and groundwater in some areas to increase. In parts of the UK it is now above the EU guide value of 50 mg l⁻¹ (Table 5.4).

There is concern that human health may be affected if these high-nitrate waters are used for drinking water. The nitrate comes from:

- High levels of fertilizer used in intensive farming to obtain high cereal yields. Some of the nitrogen in the fertilizer may not be taken up by the crop, and then may be leached from the soil, or infiltrate into groundwater.

- Spreading large quantities of manure or slurry on farmland from intensive stock-rearing.

- Effluent discharges from some sewage works, and the use of sewage sludge on farmland (Section 5.5).

The first two bullet points mean that all major intensively farmed areas are affected, particularly the cereal-growing areas of northern Europe and the USA, and the stock-rearing parts of northern Europe (Brittany, the Netherlands and Denmark).

To reduce nitrate concentrations by water treatment methods requires ion exchange or biological denitrification. Both are very expensive procedures. Other 'lateral' approaches are being used instead:

- Finding alternative sources of water — closing some boreholes and opening new, low-nitrate ones.

- Blending (diluting) high-nitrate water with that from a low-nitrate source.

- Reducing the *inputs* of nitrate into water, by using government legislation to reduce the use of fertilizers, manure and slurry in designated areas, called Nitrate Vulnerable Zones in the EU. In these zones there are compulsory restrictions to reduce nitrate leaching from the soil, encouraging farmers to change their farming operations to less intensive ones, such as switching from cereals to grassland or using buffer strips (Figure 5.17).

Figure 5.17 An experimental grass buffer strip about 20 m wide between the stream and the crop in a Nitrate Vulnerable Zone used to reduce the amounts of nitrates and other nutrients applied to the arable field from reaching the stream. The V-notch weir is used to monitor discharge and the shed houses automatic equipment to sample and assess water quality.

Groundwater seldom requires much treatment, mainly because aquifers are efficient natural filters; disinfection is usually enough. Surface water, however, presents more problems. Unpolluted river water may require straining, storage, aeration, filtration and disinfection. If the source of raw water is a poorer quality river, these treatments may have to be repeated several times. Amsterdam, for example, has the misfortune to be at the downstream end of the Rhine. To make the poor quality Rhine water palatable it is successively aerated, filtered, aerated, disinfected, aerated, filtered, stored, aerated, filtered, aerated and disinfected again. Although it may be safe to drink after all this treatment, it still occasionally tastes awful!

The Amsterdam water is river water that has been used many times on its way to the sea, as is the water from the Thames used by London. The quality of such recycled water depends on the efficiency of the sewage treatment, and in the next section we look at the processes involved.

Question 5.3

Table 5.5 gives the chemical compositions of a natural water. Would the water in Table 5.5 be a suitable source of water for (a) an EU public water supply, or (b) irrigation?

Table 5.5 Chemical compositions of a natural water from Yellowstone National Park, USA.

	Concentration/mg l^{-1}
bicarbonate	50
calcium	5
chloride	4
iron	0.1
magnesium	1
potassium	4
silica	135
sodium	28
sulphate	8
TDS	242
pH	7.6

5.5 Sewage treatment

Sewage treatment has two main aims: to control the spread of disease, by isolating the sewage so that viruses and other pathogens die, and to break down the sewage into relatively harmless substances to protect the environment into which it is discharged. In the UK around 97% of the population are connected to waste water treatment works by sewers, but this is very different on a global scale. In developing countries the figure is less than 5%; most of the urban sewage is discharged into surface waters without any form of treatment. Many cities in developing countries lack sewer systems, let alone treatment plants. Sewage is often drained into rivers or lakes that may also be used as water sources — with obvious problems for health. In Albania, for example, there are no treatment plants at all, and domestic and industrial sewage is discharged untreated into rivers and the Mediterranean Sea. For many developing countries, contaminated water containing bacteria, parasites and viruses derived from sewage is a major cause of death.

Communities situated on coasts commonly discharge untreated sewage into the sea. This is an acceptable method of disposal if the outfall is far enough offshore, if currents do not bring the sewage back to land, and if the discharge is not too great. In these circumstances, the organic matter can be broken down by bacteria in the sea. Sea discharges are not always satisfactory, however: some of the UK's beaches, for example, breach the EU Directive on bathing water quality. By 2005, 97% of UK beaches are expected to comply with the Directive.

In inland areas of industrialized countries, sewage is usually treated to reduce the amount of oxygen-consuming organic material before it is discharged into lakes or rivers. Sewage treatment aims to reduce biodegradable material and material in suspension, remove toxic materials and eliminate pathogenic bacteria. It converts sewage into a liquid **effluent**, mainly water, leaving behind a **sludge**. The discharge of effluent to streams and rivers in the UK is controlled through a system of **discharge consents** by the EA, SEPA and the EHS. These limit the total volume, the BOD and the suspended solid concentration. There is no fixed standard, as the character and use of rivers varies greatly; for example, if a small quantity of effluent is discharged into a river with a high capacity for self-purification, it may be harmless provided the effluent is not toxic. Effluents from industry often have to conform to additional standards, which may include limits on water temperature or content of toxic substances.

5.5.1 Sewage treatment processes

The processes at a sewage treatment works are relatively simple, and mostly mimic natural processes. Not all treatment works use all the treatment stages — some plants provide only preliminary and primary treatment, and tertiary treatment is rare. The processes are summarized in Figure 5.18 and amplified below:

- *Preliminary treatment* This is the mechanical removal of coarse and fine solid material. The sewage passes through screens, which trap pieces of wood, rags, wire, etc. The extracted material is usually buried, but it may be burned.

- *Primary treatment* The sewage then flows slowly through grit tanks, where particles of sand or grit settle out. Fine particles still remain suspended in the sewage, so it is passed to large primary sedimentation tanks where most of the remaining particles settle out to form a sludge. Primary treatment removes about 60–70% of suspended solids (Table 5.6). The liquid leaving the primary sedimentation tanks still contains very fine solids and dissolved matter, so secondary treatment is usually required.

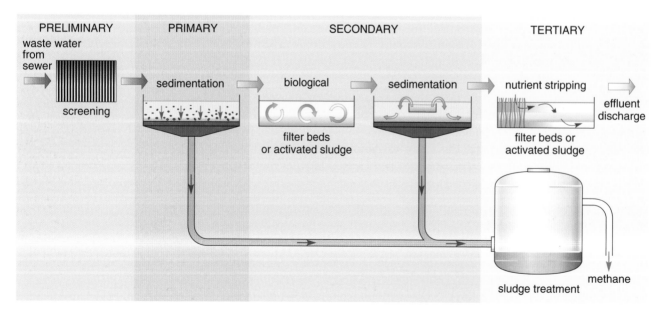

Figure 5.18 Flow diagram of the stages of treatment in a sewage treatment plant.

Table 5.6 The percentage removal (cumulative, from initial state) of constituents or characteristics of sewage after successive stages of treatment.

Constituent	Primary	Secondary	Tertiary
suspended solids	60–70	80–95	90–95
BOD	20–40	70–90	>95
phosphorus	10–30	20–40	85–97
nitrogen	10–20	20–40	20–40
E. coli bacteria	60–90	90–99	>99
viruses	30–70	90–99	>99
cadmium and zinc	5–20	20–40	40–60
copper, lead and chromium	40–60	70–90	80–89

- *Secondary treatment* This is a biological process, involving the oxidation of dissolved organic material by micro-organisms to decompose the organic compounds, a process similar to that taking place in rivers, the soil, or filter beds in water treatment works. The process is speeded up by increasing the amount of oxygen available, which can be done by two possible methods:

  Filter beds The liquid is sprayed slowly over beds of broken stones, gravel, coke or plastic (Figure 5.19), which provide a large surface area for oxidation, and the micro-organisms (mainly bacteria) living within the filter bed break down the organic matter. The liquid that collects at the base of the filter bed contains some waste products from the filter organisms. These are separated from the effluent in secondary sedimentation tanks, producing more sludge. Filter beds need very little supervision, but take up a lot of land.

  Activated sludge A sludge containing bacteria and other organisms is mixed with the liquid, and the whole mixture is agitated by paddles or has compressed air bubbled through it, to keep it well oxygenated. This process lasts about 10 hours, after which the mixture flows to sedimentation tanks where the sludge settles out from the effluent.

  Secondary treatment in addition to primary treatment removes about 70–90% of the BOD in the sewage (Table 5.6), so the effluent is usually sufficiently purified to be discharged to a river, lake or the sea.

- *Tertiary treatment* Primary and secondary treatment remove only 20–40 % of the phosphorus and nitrogen, and about half of the toxic compounds. If it is necessary to reduce plant nutrients or toxic compounds beyond these levels tertiary treatment is required, but this is very expensive and not commonly used. Various types of tertiary treatment exists, e.g. nutrient stripping, disinfection by UV light or filter membranes.

Figure 5.19 Filter beds at a waste water treatment plant. Rotating arms spray sewage onto the circular beds, where it is broken down by bacteria.

5.5.2 Sludge disposal

What to do with the remaining sludge is more of a problem. Sludge is a nasty smelling, thick liquid, about 96% water, and sewage treatment plants have to dispose of vast quantities of it — a large plant will produce over a thousand tonnes each day. Before final disposal, sludge is sometimes held in closed tanks (Figure 5.18), where, in the absence of oxygen, anaerobic bacteria further decompose the organic material, producing a relatively inoffensive digested sludge. The process takes 20 to 30 days at a temperature of around 30 °C. The gases methane and carbon dioxide are produced, and the methane can be used as a fuel to heat the tanks or to generate electricity for the treatment works. There are four main methods of sludge disposal:

- *Dumping at sea*   This needs to be carefully controlled, as the sea, like rivers and lakes, has only a limited capacity to absorb pollutants. It is particularly important to control pollution in enclosed seas such as the North Sea or the Mediterranean, where there is little water interchange with the larger oceans. The EU ended dumping at sea in 1998.

- *Farmland*   Sludge disposal on agricultural land is useful as a fertilizer and soil conditioner and it is a more convenient method of sludge disposal for sewage works that are not on the coast. Tankers are used to transport the large volumes of sludge to farms. The UK disposes of much of its sludge by this method (Figure 5.20).

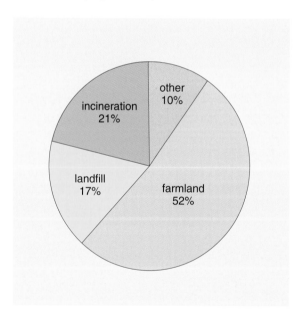

Figure 5.20   Percentage of sewage sludge disposal to different outlets in the UK, 1999/2000. 'Other' includes land reclamation, composting, energy generation and processed products.

- *Landfill*   Not all sludge is suitable for farmland. For example, sludge containing toxic waste cannot be spread on fields. Instead it is dumped in natural or artificial depressions in the ground or in trenches, where it dries and decomposes slowly (and may cause unpleasant smells), and covered with a layer of soil.

- *Incineration*   Sludge may be dried and incinerated, leaving an inert ash. This is often the most expensive option.

5.6 Summary of Chapter 5

1 Pollution is a deterioration of water quality caused by human agencies that makes the water less suitable for use than it was originally. Water does not have to be completely pure to be considered unpolluted.

2 Natural waters are not completely pure. Rainwater contains dissolved salts in relative proportions similar to those in seawater, but over a thousand times less concentrated. Rainwater contains a greater relative proportion of dissolved gases, particularly carbon dioxide, than seawater, and this makes it slightly acidic. River water has a composition different from both rainwater and seawater; it has a greater concentration of dissolved solids (TDS) than rainwater, and may contain suspended solids. Groundwater usually has slightly greater TDS values than surface water, and varies in composition, depending on the rocks through which it has passed. The TDS value of groundwater depends on the length of time the water has been in contact with rock, so slow-moving, deeper groundwater has a higher TDS value.

3 Pollution can come from many different sources, including domestic sewage, farms, industry, mining, quarrying and cooling. There are many types of pollutants, including natural organic materials, living organisms, plant nutrients, organic and inorganic chemicals, sediments and heat.

4 Water often has to be treated before it is of suitable quality for use. The quality needed depends on the use to which the water is to be put; quality standards for public water supplies are set by the WHO, the EU and some individual countries; but the quality required for industrial water and irrigation water can vary.

5 Sewage treatment aims to reduce the amount of organic and suspended solid material present, remove toxic materials and eliminate pathogenic bacteria, mainly by settlement or biological processes. The effluent is discharged into rivers, lakes or the sea, and the remaining sludge may be dumped at sea (but not in the EU), disposed of on farmland, dumped in landfills or incinerated.

Activity 5.2

At the beginning of this book it was stated that water is probably the most important physical resource that we use. We often take its presence for granted in the UK: for most of us it arrives painlessly in our home out of a tap and we can easily dispose of it by pouring or flushing it away. However, how much do you really know about your own water supply and sewage disposal? Are you drinking groundwater or river water? Is it recycled? What is its quality? Where does your sewage go? How much does it cost you? In this activity you can consider all these questions, although you may need to contact your water supply and sewage disposal company to answer some of them.

(a) Do you have a piped water supply? (1% or so of homes in the UK do not.)

(b) What is the source of your water? Perhaps there are several sources. (Does it come from a reservoir, a river, groundwater or a combination?)

(c) Where is your local water treatment works for water supply and what processes does it use?

(d) What is the chemical analysis of your water? Are there any particularly high concentrations, over or near EU limits?

(e) Do you have a water meter?

(f) What was the cost per person for water supply to your home last year?

(g) Is your home connected to sewers, or do you have a septic tank or cesspit?

(h) If your home is connected to sewers, where is your local waste water treatment works and what processes take place there?

(i) How does the waste water treatment works dispose of the effluent (into which river, lake, or sea) and the sludge (farmland, landfill or incineration)?

(j) What was the cost per person for sewage disposal from your home last year?

EXTENDING WATER RESOURCES

6

Existing supplies of water will have to be used in different ways, or new sources will have to be found, to satisfy a greater demand for water in the future. This chapter looks at alternative methods of exploiting water resources by water transfer, estuary storage, and conjunctive use, and also at methods for creating new supplies of fresh water by desalination and rain-making.

6.1 Water transfer

Water transfer is the transfer of water from one river catchment to another. Transfer can take place by river diversion, pipeline or even by sea tanker. There is often a surplus of water in one area and too little in another — both on a small scale within a country, on a larger, continental scale and even on a global scale. Water transfer is one method of increasing the supply to areas with too little water. For example, Manchester is supplied with water piped from reservoirs in the Lake District (Figure 6.1) and the industrial cities of South Yorkshire are supplied with water from rivers to the north through the Yorkshire Grid Scheme, which uses rivers and large mains to transfer water from one river catchment area to another.

Figure 6.1 Haweswater reservoir in the English Lake District, which provides water for Manchester.

On a larger scale, water is transferred between major river catchments in the south-western USA by means of large canals, pumping stations and tunnels. An enormous quantity of water, around $5.5 \times 10^9 \, \text{m}^3$ a year, is transferred 300 km or so from the Colorado River basin to California, where it is used mainly for irrigation in the agricultural areas of southern California, but also for public water supply in Los Angeles, San Diego and other cities. Half of all the water used in southern California comes from the Colorado, and California would like even more but the river is unable to supply it.

On an international scale, the southern USA would like to transfer water from Canada. Every few years, plans to divert massive amounts of Canadian water to water-scarce areas of the United States by tanker, pipeline, or rerouting of the natural river systems, are considered. One of the largest proposed diversion projects was called the GRAND Canal — the Great Recycling And Northern Development Canal. It originally called for the building of a dam across James Bay at the Hudson Bay entrance to create a giant freshwater reservoir out of James Bay and the twenty rivers flowing into it. This water would then be diverted south by river and canal through the Great Lakes to the south of the USA.

The North American Water And Power Alliance (NAWAPA) was a similar scheme. The general idea of NAWAPA was to collect surplus water from areas of high precipitation in the north-western part of the North American continent and distribute it to water-scarce areas of Canada, the USA and northern Mexico.

Box 6.1   The Snowy Mountains Scheme

One of the world's largest-scale national water transfer schemes in existence is the Snowy Mountains Scheme in Australia, where water is lacking in the vast, low-lying interior, but the eastern rim of highlands has plentiful rainfall. Unfortunately the rivers of the highlands flow eastward into the Pacific Ocean mainly unused. The Snowy Mountains Scheme traps part of the flow of two of these rivers in reservoirs (Figure 6.2). This water is then pumped through tunnels and aqueducts to the west side of the Snowy Mountains, to the Murray and Tumut River systems, increasing the water available to Australia's interior. Because of the difference in altitude between the intake in the highlands and the outlet in the interior, the Scheme generates enough hydroelectricity to pay for the operating costs.

The Scheme was completed in 1974, taking 25 years to build, at a cost of £400 million. It diverts an average of $2.36 \times 10^9 \, \text{m}^3$ of water a year to the interior, and the hydroelectric power output is 3754 MW (equivalent to the power output of almost four nuclear power stations). The system has the flexibility to allow water to be released from reservoirs only when needed during the dry season, or to allow water to be transferred between reservoirs.

Although the discharge of the Murray and Tumut Rivers was successfully increased, there have been large environmental impacts associated with the scheme; land drowned by reservoirs, higher water tables, increased leaching of salts into rivers, and ecological changes in the river basins.

Figure 6.2   (a) The Snowy Mountains Scheme in Australia. (b) A diagrammatic cross-section (not an accurate section). Some of the reservoirs have been lettered (A–E) so that you can identify the same reservoirs in (a) and (b).

Map (a):

Tumut R.

10 km

N

Tantagara Reservoir

Tooma R.

L. Eucumbene

Eucumbene R.

E

D

Swampy Plain R.

Geehi R.

B

A

C

Murray R.

Snowy R.

land over 1500 m
power station
pumping station
dam
tunnel or aqueduct

(a)

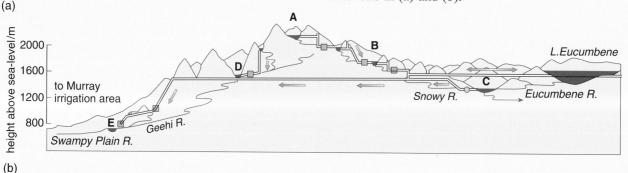

(b)

A series of dams and power stations in Alaska and northern British Columbia would collect water and provide power to pump this water up to a reservoir in the Rocky Mountains in south-eastern British Columbia. From the Rocky Mountains reservoir, water would be pumped to another reservoir in Idaho. From there, the water would flow by gravity to the western States.

None of the North American diversion and pipeline schemes were implemented nor look likely to be in the future. The most obvious reason for this is the capital cost of the schemes, due to the massive engineering works involved in diverting water on a continental scale. The value of the water, especially if used for irrigation, is insufficient to repay or justify the construction cost. The second reason is the difficulty of reaching international agreement to go ahead with the scheme, and there is also an unwillingness to depend on another country for water. The final reason is environmental: the schemes attracted massive opposition on environmental grounds, for drowning land and towns, destruction of wildlife habitats and even the possibility of changing the climate.

Although large-scale international water transfers by diversion and pipeline have not yet been implemented, international transfer on a smaller, more flexible scale is being used (Box 6.2).

Water used to be regarded as a resource with a high *place value*, but international water transfers indicate that it can at times be a low place value resource. Large-scale water transfer is a very expensive way of increasing

Box 6.2   Tankering, towing water and icebergs

Among other schemes, Canada is transporting water to the Bahamas using ships as water tankers, Alaska has sent water to Japan and Turkey sends water to Cyprus. Water could also be towed, as well as tankered, in large plastic bags. There is little capital cost involved, and transport by sea is cheap. The environmental effects are minimal: no land need be drowned.

A large proportion of the Earth's fresh water is in the polar ice caps (Section 2.1), but so far this has not been used for water resources. Ice is formed in both polar regions, but 90% of it is in Antarctica and most of the rest is in the Greenland ice cap. The problem with using these frozen assets is that the ice is in the wrong place. To be of use as a water resource, it would have to be transported large distances to lower-latitude water-deficient areas such as western South America and Australia, or even across the Equator from the Antarctic to southern California or the Middle East. The most convenient ice to transport would be floating icebergs.

Antarctic icebergs are flat slabs 200–250 m thick and a kilometre long on average, which have broken off from the floating ice shelves that surround the Antarctic land area. Greenland icebergs form by breaking off from valley glaciers where these glaciers border the sea; they have a wide range of sizes, but are generally smaller than the Antarctic icebergs and more irregular in shape. Icebergs float with most of the iceberg beneath the sea surface, which gives them a draught much greater than that of ships and prevents them travelling in shallow water. It is technically possible to tow icebergs; offshore oil rig operators have moved them short distances when there has been the possibility of collision with oil rigs.

The cost of water from icebergs is difficult to estimate, because of uncertainties about the energy required for towing and the rate of melting, and icebergs have not yet (2004) been used as a water source. Iceberg water will probably never be cheap, but it could prove to be less expensive than water from desalination or from long-distance water transfer.

water resources, but may be necessary when there are no alternative local sources. The cost can be comparable with that of desalination (Section 6.4), and while desalination may be a preferable alternative in many areas, it is energy-intensive and restricted to coastal areas.

6.2 Estuary storage

Estuaries may be used as reservoirs to store water. The water in estuaries is a mixture of fresh river water and seawater. To store fresh water, a barrage can be built across the mouth of the estuary to keep seawater out of the whole estuary, or embankments can be constructed, enclosing smaller river-fed freshwater reservoirs within the estuary.

Estuary storage has many advantages. It avoids flooding large areas of land for reservoirs, and the large lake created in an estuary could also be used for recreation. Cities are often located around estuaries, so water would be available where there is a demand for it. It is sometimes possible to combine an estuary storage scheme with a road or rail link across the estuary, to improve communications in the area. On the other hand, estuary storage also has many disadvantages. The water is stored at the lowest point of the river, at sea level, and it would have to be pumped to all users. River water often contains a high proportion of effluent at river mouths, so the water is usually of poor quality and would require expensive treatment. A barrier would restrict navigation. There may also be ecological problems as estuaries with tidal mudflats are the feeding grounds of many coastal birds and other animals.

There are two large estuary storage schemes in the Netherlands where water storage is combined with land reclamation, flood protection and communication links across barrages. The Zuyder Zee in the Netherlands used to be a large tidal lagoon, and has been converted into a number of polders (land reclaimed from the sea, below sea level, e.g. Figure 6.3) and a large freshwater lake, the Ijsselmeer. The Rhine delta scheme involves barrages across the channels in the delta, a combination of flood protection and water storage.

In Britain, proposals were made in the 1960s for barrages to be built across Morecambe Bay to provide more water for the Manchester area, across the Dee estuary for Liverpool, and across the Wash for East Anglia. However, all the proposals for estuary storage in Britain were dropped in the late 1970s because of their expense and inflexibility, and concern about environmental changes.

Figure 6.3   Land reclaimed from the sea (a polder) in the Netherlands. The windmill was used to pump water out of the area.

6.3 Conjunctive use

Conjunctive use is the combined use of surface water resources and groundwater, in a unified way, to optimize resource use and minimize the adverse effects of using a single source. It exploits the storage capacity of an aquifer and the ease of transport of water by a river. The aquifer is used to store surface water when there is an excess of it and it would otherwise be wasted, such as in winter. The river is used to transport water from the aquifer to where it is needed when the river discharge is too low on its own, as often happens in summer. Conjunctive use can also reduce abstraction from rivers when the discharge is low by using groundwater instead.

The storage of excess surface water underground in an aquifer is a type of conjunctive use called **managed aquifer recharge**. This makes the most of excess water by directing it into the ground where it can be stored for future use. Underground storage has many advantages over surface storage: no land is taken up by reservoirs, there is no evaporation loss, and capital costs are much lower. However, managed aquifer recharge is not a simple process, and it is difficult to do on a useful scale; it cannot absorb large volumes of flood water in a short time. It involves transferring water from the surface to underground, either by dispersing it over the surface to increase infiltration, or through aquifer injection wells.

Surface dispersal involves diverting the water into an unlined canal or shallow lagoon in permeable sediments or rock so that the water can percolate downwards into the aquifer (Figure 6.4). It works best in areas with highly permeable soils and unconfined aquifers, and where land is inexpensive.

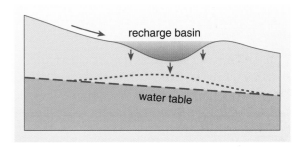

Aquifer injection wells are used to recharge aquifers directly. Direct injection of water through wells is more expensive than basin recharge but is used when there is no suitable land for a recharge basin, or with confined aquifers. **Aquifer storage and recovery (ASR)** schemes (Box 6.3) use the same borehole to inject and recover water. While most ASR systems are designed to store water during the wet season and recover it during the following dry season, some are established for water banking, where recovery may not take place for many years.

Figure 6.4 A managed aquifer recharge basin can increase recharge by slowing the overland flow and allowing more time for infiltration. The dashed line is the new water table after recharge.

Box 6.3   ASR in the Thames Valley

ASR is used in the Thames Valley area, north of London. Here water is often in short supply in summer, and it would be useful to be able to use more groundwater from the underlying Chalk and Basal Sands aquifer (Figure 3.21). In the 1970s an artificial recharge scheme using injection wells was started in the Lee Valley area to the north of London, where the aquifer is intensively exploited. The water used for recharge is from the Rivers Thames and Lee at times of excess flow in winter. It is treated to drinking water standards before recharge (when spare treatment capacity is available) so that there is no danger of polluting good-quality groundwater. The Scheme is designed to recharge the aquifer artificially over an area of 50 km^2 and provide an extra resource of 10^5 m^3 a day during drought conditions.

Storm runoff, which would otherwise be lost to the sea, can be used for managed aquifer recharge, especially in arid areas. In the Central Valley of California, storm runoff is trapped in alluvial sediments. On Long Island, New York, aquifers are recharged through sands and gravels, which also helps to prevent flooding. In some areas it is possible to use sewage effluent for managed aquifer recharge, as the polluting substances in the water are removed by biological processes during infiltration. However, it is very easy to pollute an aquifer, especially if the effluent contains industrial waste. Another problem of artificial recharge is that fine sediment in the water can quickly clog the pores in an aquifer, reducing the natural rate of recharge from lakes, lagoons and wells.

Another type of conjunctive use is the use of groundwater to increase the flow of a river, called **river augmentation** (Box 6.4). Its advantage is that a river can be used to convey groundwater to its destination without the need to build a pipeline. The effect is similar to river regulation, except that the water is stored underground instead of in surface reservoirs. A disadvantage is that the high-quality groundwater is mixed with poorer-quality river water and will require more extensive treatment before it can be used than would have been required had it travelled through a pipeline.

Groundwater and surface water are closely linked: groundwater maintains the baseflow of rivers, and water in rivers can infiltrate into the ground. The abstraction of surface water and groundwater cannot be planned in isolation — one will affect the other. For example, the abstraction of groundwater can reduce the baseflow contribution to rivers by lowering the water table. If carefully planned, however, the conjunctive use of rivers and groundwater can even out the seasonal variations in river flow. In the summer when the river flow is low, water is pumped from the aquifer into the river, so that more water can be drawn from the river downstream. The wells must be far enough from the river (Figure 6.5, well A) for the drawdown around them not to make the water table slope away from the river, or water will flow back towards the well from the river (well B). Pumping from wells also intercepts some of the natural baseflow to the river.

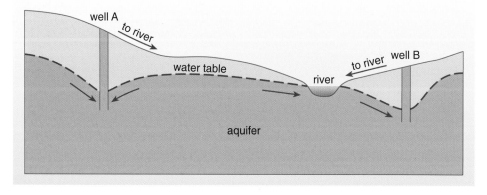

Figure 6.5 River augmentation using a river and an aquifer. The arrows below the water table show the directions of groundwater flow (in the direction of slope of the water table). Wells must be far enough away from the river (well A) for the level of the water table at the river to be unaffected by the well drawdown. If a well were too close to a river (well B), water could flow from the river to the well, recycling the water put into the river and reducing the net gain. The net gain is also reduced as some of the natural baseflow to the river will be intercepted by the wells.

The amount by which natural river flow is augmented by pumping is referred to as the **net gain**, usually expressed as a percentage of the pumped quantity. The net gain is never 100% as some of the additional water in the river always infiltrates back into the aquifer. River augmentation schemes normally show a net gain to the river of between 40% and 70% of the water put in from the aquifer.

Box 6.4 The Shropshire Groundwater Scheme

Triassic sandstones are the major aquifer in the English Midlands, and are exploited intensively for water supply. The only area with substantial unused reserves in the aquifer is in north Shropshire, in the Severn Basin.

The River Severn is the main component of the water resources strategy in the West Midlands (Figure 6.6). The river is regulated by water from the Clywedog and Vyrnwy reservoirs in Wales in the summer months, but the regulated flow is insufficient both in dry summers and to supply future demands (Section 4.3 and Figure 4.10).

A phased scheme of river augmentation to the River Severn from groundwater in the Triassic sandstones in north Shropshire was started in the 1970s. At the moment (2004) the scheme can supply up to $10^5 \, \text{m}^3$ a day during the summer months when necessary. The net gain is at least 65%. Further phases of the scheme are due to be developed at a pace consistent with demand and if all phases are implemented it could supply $3.3 \times 10^5 \, \text{m}^3$ a day. Not only is this scheme cheaper than building a new reservoir, but it is cheap to operate, is less environmentally destructive, and can be implemented in stages, depending on demand.

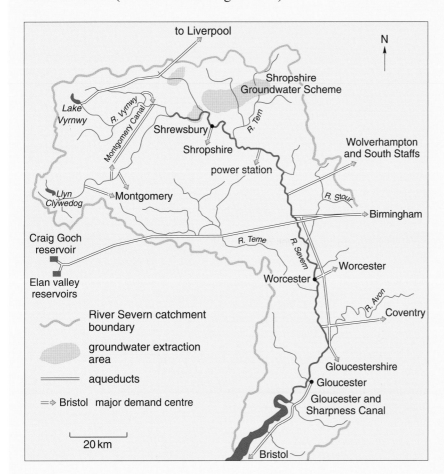

Figure 6.6 The Shropshire Groundwater Scheme is part of the River Severn water resources system.

6.4   Desalination

Desalination removes dissolved minerals (including but not limited to common salt) from seawater, brackish water or treated waste water. The amount of water in the sea is enormous, but before it can be used for water resources, dissolved salts in the water must be removed or substantially reduced. Desalination of seawater could produce unlimited supplies of fresh water and could solve many water resources problems if it were possible to do it inexpensively. Unfortunately, desalination is an expensive process, the water produced generally costing more than from other sources, as it has high capital costs and requires a lot of energy, so it is not usually the first choice for a water supply. However, it is used if there is no other source available. Other disadvantages are that a large amount of saline water is required, which generally restricts the process to coastal areas (although saline groundwater and water from inland seas can also be used as the raw material), and that disposal of the concentrated brine produced may be difficult.

There are various processes for desalinating water. The one most commonly used is *distillation*, which is similar to the natural evaporation of seawater in the hydrological cycle. Many arid countries receive large amounts of solar energy and this can be used as the energy source in a solar distillation process. However, solar distillation needs large areas of solar stills and produces only small quantities of water — a maximum of only 5 litres per day for each square metre of still area. It is usually used only in remote villages in arid developing countries. Larger quantities of water can be produced by distillation plants where the saline water is heated by more concentrated energy sources, and plants producing over 10^3 m^3 per day are common. Most of the larger plants, such as the 10^6 m^3 per day plant in Jubail, Saudi Arabia, use the distillation method. The efficiency of distillation plants (ratio of usable output water to input water) ranges from 15–50%.

Another important desalination process is *reverse osmosis* (Figure 6.7). This uses high pressure to force saline water through a semipermeable plastic membrane, which filters out both suspended and dissolved substances. Reverse osmosis is more suitable for desalinating water with a lower salinity than seawater. The world's largest reverse osmosis plant is under construction and due to be commissioned in 2005 at Ashkelon, Israel: it will produce 3×10^5 m^3 per day. The project is expected to cost US\$200 million, and produce water at a production cost of around US\$0.5 m^{-3}.

Figure 6.7   Inside the Eilat reverse osmosis desalination plant in Israel. This produces 8×10^3 m^3 of water per day.

Energy costs are a substantial part of the cost of desalinated water (except for solar stills, which use free solar energy but have relatively high capital costs per cubic metre and low outputs). It takes a considerable quantity of energy to desalinate a cubic metre of water by distillation, around 300 MJ m^{-3} for seawater, so the cost of desalination by this means depends directly on the *energy cost*. If a country has a cheap source of energy, desalination may be practical. In California, which has a number of desalination plants, the selling cost of the water is US\$1–4 m^{-3}. A desalination plant which began operation in 1992 in Santa Barbara in California had a capital cost of US\$36 million for 12×10^6 m^3 a year, at a selling price of US\$2.4 m^{-3}. However, this plant has now been decommissioned (2004) as this water proved to be more expensive than other water sources.

Desalination is generally used only where there is no other possible source of water, as all other sources would be cheaper, with the possible exception of long-distance water transfer schemes. Desalination is used in wealthy but arid coastal areas, where it is economic to pay a higher price for water; Saudi Arabia produces 70% of its drinking water by desalination. The Arabian Peninsula and Iran, for example, have a greater desalination capacity than all the rest of the world, using energy from their abundant oil resources to produce water. The four countries with over 10^6 m^3 per day desalination capacity are Saudi Arabia, the USA, the United Arab Emirates and Kuwait. The UK, for comparison, has a current capacity (2004) of about 10^5 m^3 per day. However, this is likely to increase in the near future, as there are plans for London's first-ever desalination plant. The £200 million project is planned for completion in 2007/2008, to help with supplies during drought periods. This will convert water from the tidal River Thames (less saline than seawater) into drinking water. The plant will have a maximum treatment capacity of 1.5×10^5 m^3 per day, using reverse osmosis.

Other areas where desalination is common include islands with limited amounts of water because of their necessarily limited catchment areas, and where desalination is the only method of increasing these resources. In many cases the desalination plants are only used as back-ups to the normal supply, or to meet seasonal demands. Jersey (capacity 6.8×10^3 m^3 per day, installed 1969) and the Isles of Scilly (2.2×10^2 m^3 per day, installed 1992), for example, have the only reasonably large-scale desalination plants in the UK at present (2004), used to meet the summer demand from holiday visitors.

If the technology improves, or the cost of other water resources increases, desalination is likely to become more economic and therefore used more. A distillation plant built in combination with a power station, using the waste heat from the power station to drive desalination, has much lower running costs, and these combined plants are likely to become more common. Desalination will probably become increasingly important for the richer arid coastal countries and as an emergency method of supply in other areas in times of drought, when there is no alternative to the high cost of desalinated water. But for irrigation use, and for poorer countries, it will be too expensive to use even in times of drought.

Question 6.1

If the capital cost were repaid over 10 years, what would be the capital cost contribution per cubic metre to the selling cost of water from the desalination plants in (a) Santa Barbara, and (b) the Isles of Scilly (capital cost of £250 000) ignoring interest charges on the capital? Comment on the difference between the two values. Use the conversion US$1 = £0.55.

6.5 Rain-making

'Everybody complains about the weather but nobody does anything about it.'

(Mark Twain)

These days, Mark Twain would be wrong; many people are trying to change the weather, mostly to influence precipitation. Attempting to induce an increase in precipitation by artificial means is called **rain-making**. Clouds consist of minute droplets of water, but not all clouds produce rain, and when it rains, it doesn't always pour; only a small fraction of the water droplets in each cloud reaches the ground as precipitation. So the idea that human intervention — a rain-dance, perhaps — might encourage a cloud to give up a little extra water has been around since ancient times. More recently, would-be rain-makers have attempted direct intervention, by delivering various chemicals from aeroplanes in an effort to wring more rain from the clouds, a practice known as 'cloud seeding'.

There is no possibility of rain-making in cloudless arid areas; the main condition for rain-making is to have water in the atmosphere as clouds. For rain to fall, the water droplets in clouds must condense around small particles of solid material, until it forms drops heavy enough to fall as rain (Section 2.2). If there are no solid particles to act as nuclei for condensation, there will be no rainfall. Cloud-seeding supplies nuclei around which condensation can begin. This will only work for clouds where the water content is high enough for the air to be supersaturated — and the warmer the air, the more water droplets it can contain before the conditions for precipitation are reached. The substances used to seed clouds are commonly silver iodide, common salt or dry ice (solid carbon dioxide). The substance is released into the cloud from the ground (Figure 6.8), aircraft (a more expensive method) or rockets.

Figure 6.8   Ground generator of silver iodide for cloud seeding at Bridgeport, California, USA.

Rain-making was first developed in the 1940s. One of the first times it was used successfully was in Ontario, Canada in 1948. A large fire was raging in Northern Ontario. When dry ice was seeded into clouds above the fire a rainstorm developed that helped put out the blaze.

This method was also used to make snow. In Saint Moritz, Switzerland, in 1949, a hotel owner needed snow for his skiing guests and hired a 'cloudbuster' to make it. Dry ice was thrown out of an aeroplane above clouds over Saint Moritz. Snow did fall, but unfortunately for Saint Moritz it came down to the north instead, over the ski runs of Davos, a rival town.

The effectiveness of rain-making is difficult to evaluate. It is hard to tell, for example, how much rain would have fallen anyway; rainfall often has a high natural variation from year to year. In order to be certain that cloud seeding is really increasing rainfall, researchers have to compare seeded clouds with similar, unseeded ones, which is very difficult to do. In 2003 the National Research Council of the USA concluded that there was still no conclusive proof that cloud seeding works. The greatest scepticism involves summer rainfall, where rain-making seems least likely to be successful. But the Research Council noted a strong suggestion of a positive effect on winter precipitation in mountain areas. So ski resorts regularly seed clouds to boost snowfall. Power companies, farmers and cities do it and bank water for later in the spring thaw. The Snowy Mountains Scheme in Australia also uses it in winter to increase reservoir levels.

So despite no conclusive proof that it actually works, anecdotal evidence of the effectiveness of rain-making has led to its adoption in more than 40 countries around the world. Part of the reason for its use must be that the extra water it produces is very cheap in comparison to other methods mentioned in this chapter, of the order of US$0.001 m^{-3}, about a thousand times less expensive than desalination, for example. This is mainly because rain-making does not need a large capital investment.

So why isn't rain-making used more often? The main reason is that if the clouds are not there, you cannot seed them, so this cuts out most of the arid areas of the world where it would be of most use. Another reason is that it may not work for summer rainfall. There is also a problem of identifying whether it has worked; in 2000 in Utah, USA, for example, cloud seeding projects were estimated to have increased snowfall by between 7 and 20% — a lot of valuable water — but within the annual variability of precipitation.

Another concern is that artificially removing water from the atmosphere in one area may reduce the precipitation elsewhere; rain-making may simply redistribute the precipitation. But this is to regard the atmospheric system as a fixed pool of water, which it is not; the atmosphere is a dynamic system and does not behave as simply. There seems to be no evidence of a decrease in precipitation downwind of rain-making projects.

Yet another concern is that if a cloud is moving when it is seeded, the water may not be precipitated at the intended place, as we have seen for Saint Moritz. However, this is not a problem if seeding is done to supply a large area.

6.6 Conservation

An alternative approach to extending water resources is by water conservation. One way of doing this is to use less water, more *efficiently*. In countries where water is available at the turn of a tap, water is wasted in many ways — by water-inefficient appliances and unaware users. Industry may also use water inefficiently, and so does most irrigation, where water is transported to fields through unlined, uncovered canals, and used in surface furrow irrigation (Figure 6.9). Changes in technology can be used to reduce inefficient water use.

Figure 6.9 Surface furrow irrigation, in Jordan. Water flows in channels under gravity, infiltrating the soil. This is a very inefficient form of irrigation, as much of the water is wasted through evaporation or infiltration into the soil out of reach of plant roots.

Recycling water can also extend the available water resource. For example, power stations are often major users of water to cool the steam that has driven the turbines. This steam is produced from very expensive demineralized water, so recycling it makes economic sense. Power stations cool the steam in two main ways: direct cooling, where large quantities of cooling water are pumped through the cooling system and returned to its source (used mainly when there is a plentiful supply of water on lakes or a coastline), or indirect cooling, where the cooling water itself is cooled and recycled through cooling towers (Figure 6.10). Not all the cooling water can be recycled; some is evaporated by this process.

Figure 6.10   Cooling towers of the 2 GW Cottam coal-fired power station, Nottinghamshire. This uses water from the River Trent, recycling most of it, except for that evaporated in the water droplet plumes above the cooling towers.

Another method of water conservation is *substitution*: using alternatives instead of water. On a global scale this will make little difference, as most water (70%; Section 1.1) is used for agriculture, mainly for irrigation, which is a non-substitutable use. However, on a local scale, particularly for many industrial purposes, substitution is possible. Unfortunately, alternatives to water are often more expensive and/or less efficient. For example, power stations can use a 'dry' cooling tower instead of the 'wet' cooling tower described above; dry cooling works like a car radiator, using air as a coolant instead of water (if you see a working cooling tower without the plume of evaporating water over it, it is a dry cooling tower). However, this substitution comes at a cost; wet towers cost about US$20 million each, whereas dry towers cost about US$35 million, and a major power station usually has between six and eight of these towers.

The last, and most fundamental, conservation technique is *changing practice*: to change from a water-consuming practice to one that uses less or no water. On a small scale, for example, homes in areas of low rainfall could use only desert plants in their gardens, requiring no watering. On a larger scale, a change for industrialized countries in their consumption of food, to a diet including more cereals and vegetables and less meat, may reduce the water used for agriculture, as it requires far more water per kilogram of meat protein produced than it does for cereal or vegetable protein. The need for irrigation water could be reduced by growing more crops that need a large amount of water in areas that already have sufficient natural rainfall. For example, many salad vegetables in UK supermarkets are imported from hotter countries where they are grown using scarce groundwater for irrigation. At the same time in the UK, agricultural land where similar crops could be rain-fed is designated as 'set aside' and not used.

Imported salad vegetables are an example of importing **virtual water**, which is the water used to produce the goods that a country imports. The virtual water concept is often used in a discussion of arid countries such as those in the Middle East. If, for example, it needs 1000 tonnes of water to produce one tonne of wheat then an arid but relatively rich country like Saudi Arabia can choose whether to use 1000 tonnes of water and grow the wheat itself or simply import the tonne of wheat. If it does the latter then it has saved the water; in effect it has imported 1000 tonnes of 'virtual' water. So a wealthy country does not need to be self-sufficient in producing food or manufactured articles. It becomes more relevant when considering the importation of food from places like Africa into countries such as the UK. Here we can grow a great many crops using rain-fed agriculture; when we import vegetables or cereals we are in effect importing virtual water into what is a relatively water-rich country. The situation becomes more absurd if the imports come from relatively arid countries and are grown using scarce water resources, for example lettuces from Spain or asparagus from Israel.

In most countries, the response to water shortages is to augment supplies, and in the short-term manage demand by prohibiting use (e.g. hosepipes), cutting off supplies for part of the day or using standpipes, and exhorting the public to use less water. These are often effective in the short-term, but are costly and inconvenient to users, and do not take into account the relative value of water to different consumers. Where water is provided to users at a price less than the supply cost — the situation common in most parts of the world — there is little incentive for conservation; price is a tool that can be used to make users value their water supply.

All the methods of conservation considered in this section are possible, but the extent to which they are used depends on the price of water; raising the selling price will encourage more efficiency in water use, more recycling, more substitution and changing practice. Their use will also be consequent on the method chosen and the ability of people to pay for it. In developed countries conservation will depend on our determination, or not, to change our lifestyles to achieve sustainability of water resources. Will it happen? Would you, for example, be willing to give up your dishwasher or lawn, install a water butt, pay more for many manufactured products, or eat less meat?

6.7   Summary of Chapter 6

1   To supplement the water from rivers, lakes, reservoirs and aquifers, the demand for water could be met by water transfer, estuary storage, conjunctive use, desalination, rain-making and conservation.

2   Water transfer takes water from an area of surplus to an area of deficit. It has the disadvantages that it is very expensive to transport water large distances and that it may cause environmental side-effects.

3   Storing water in an estuary makes it possible to use water that would otherwise be lost to the sea. It avoids flooding large areas of land for reservoirs, and the water is available where there is a demand for it. The disadvantages are that water has to be pumped up to land, the quality will be poor, estuary navigation may be restricted and there may be ecological consequences.

4   Conjunctive use is the combined use of surface water resources and groundwater to provide a better or more flexible water resource. Two types of conjunctive use are managed aquifer recharge and river augmentation. Managed aquifer recharge is the replenishment of an aquifer in excess of

natural infiltration, by storing surface water underground when surface water is abundant. River augmentation is used to increase the flow of a river at times of low discharge. The aquifer and river can each be used directly, but at different times of year.

5   Desalination makes seawater usable for water supplies. The process consumes a lot of energy, so it is one of the most expensive ways of producing fresh water.

6   Rain-making is an artificially induced means to increase precipitation. It can only be done in certain circumstances, if there is an excess of water vapour in clouds in the atmosphere which can be seeded to provide nuclei around which water droplets can condense. There is no evidence that it can produce a long-term increase in precipitation, but it is used in many countries to increase winter precipitation.

7   Conservation is an alternative approach to extending water resources, either by greater efficiency in using water, by recycling, by substitution, or by changing practices.

WATER IN THE UK

7.1 The UK water supply

The water industry in the UK is complex, and its organization differs in each part of the UK.

Water supply and sewerage

England and Wales   Water services are provided by the private sector. Ten privatized companies deliver both water and sewerage services, while 15 water supply companies provide drinking water to their customers. The full cost of water and sewerage is met by the customers; this includes replacing old mains and sewers, and satisfying EU regulations on water quality. In addition, the private companies are expected to make a profit.

Scotland   Scottish Water is the single water authority. It supplies water and sewerage services to the whole of Scotland. Scottish Water is answerable to the Scottish Executive but is structured and managed as a private company.

Northern Ireland   Services remain in the public sector — the Water Service is an Executive Agency within the Department for Regional Development.

Economic regulation

Because water companies and authorities do not have to compete for domestic customers and compete only in a limited way for industrial customers, the prices they charge customers need to be regulated.

England and Wales   The Office of Water Services (OFWAT) has the duty to protect customers' interests while ensuring that the privately owned water companies carry out and finance their operations properly.

Scotland   The Water Commissioner oversees the performance of Scottish Water, their charging policy and service standards.

Northern Ireland   No separate regulator currently exists (2004).

Environmental regulation

The water industry is dependent upon the natural environment and also has a huge impact on it. The industry abstracts or takes water from rivers, reservoirs or aquifers, then treats it and pumps it to customers. It then collects the waste water, cleans it and discharges it back into rivers and seas.

England and Wales   The Environment Agency (EA) protects the environment in England and Wales. It has the duty to control discharges to rivers and seas, conserve water resources, prevent pollution and promote conservation.

Scotland   The Scottish Environment Protection Agency has powers and duties similar to those of the EA.

Northern Ireland   This is carried out by the Water Service and is monitored by the Environment and Heritage Service, part of the Department of the Environment.

Drinking water quality

The water suppliers carry out tests for water quality. Failures must be reported to the appropriate body.

England and Wales   The Drinking Water Inspectorate (DWI) is an independent, government-appointed regulator. The DWI implements standards and maximum permissible levels for the various chemicals in drinking water and can prosecute companies that fail to meet those standards.

Scotland and Northern Ireland   Water quality is the responsibility of government — the Scottish Executive and the Northern Ireland Water Service.

The quantities of fresh water abstracted for various purposes in England and Wales are given in Table 7.1. Water is abstracted under licences from the EA, issued on the basis of the reasonable needs of the public, industry and agriculture and availability of supplies.

Table 7.1   The quantities of fresh water (non-tidal surface water and groundwater) abstracted for different uses in England and Wales in 2001. (DEFRA, 2004)

Water use	Quantity/10^6 m^3 per day
public water supply	16.23
electricity supply industry	18.07
agriculture (includes irrigation and fish farming)	4.66
other industry	3.59
other purposes	0.56
total	43.11

Question 7.1

Calculate the total water abstracted in litres per person per day in England and Wales for 2001. Take the population as 50 million.

The public water supply is the water abstracted, purified and distributed through water mains to houses, offices, some industries and farms by the water companies. The other types of users given in Table 7.1 get much of their water directly from rivers or the ground without going through the treatment works and distribution system of the public water supply. Industry, power stations and farms often do not require high-quality water, so it is cheaper to abstract water directly than to use the more expensive, high-quality public water supply. In England and Wales the direct abstraction of water is permitted only where it is licensed by the EA, which has to ensure that there is enough water available and that it will not affect other abstractions. For example, if an industry or power station takes water directly from a river, the EA has to make sure that there is still enough water in the river at all times, and will license abstraction only up to a certain quantity. Direct abstraction is not restricted to industry: in principle there is nothing to stop you digging a well in your garden for your own domestic water supply.

As Table 7.1 shows, the largest use of water is for electricity generation (Section 6.6). Because of the enormous quantities of water required, power stations are situated on major rivers, lakes or on the coast. The main use of water is for cooling, and this water can be of low quality. Even more water is obtained from estuaries (brackish water) and the sea (saline water). The water used for cooling is returned to its source relatively quickly but some 5 °C warmer. There are considerable year-to-year fluctuations in the amount of water used for electricity generation, which we will look at in more detail in Section 7.2. Some power stations recycle cooling water; this is not a continuous yearly demand but is a 'one-off' abstraction that stays within the cooling systems and is never returned.

Another use of water in electricity generation is for raising steam in boilers, to convert thermal energy first into mechanical and then into electrical energy. Boilers require high-quality water, but only in relatively small amounts.

Figure 7.1 The spray irrigation of vegetables.

Direct abstraction by industry generally reduced during the 1980s, falling by 42% between 1980 and 1988. It increased slightly after 1998 (again, we will examine this in more detail in Section 7.2). The main causes for the reduction were the more efficient use of water, including recycling, and changes in the structure of British industry, including the contraction of some of the major water-using industries, such as steel-making.

Agriculture consumes only a small proportion of the total water abstracted (Table 7.1), although, on a global scale, irrigation is the greatest use of water. There is sufficient rainfall for agriculture over Wales and the western and northern parts of England so irrigation is used mainly in the drier central, southern and eastern parts of England, particularly in East Anglia (Figure 7.1). Irrigation water is usually obtained by direct abstraction from rivers and boreholes and it can be of low quality.

A significant and increasing proportion of the UK's root and vegetable harvest is produced using irrigation; for example 36% of the UK potato crop is currently (2004) irrigated. The amount of water abstracted for irrigation is greater in dry summers, and there is also a long-term increase. The installation of irrigation equipment is increasing, partly in response to supermarket demand for a consistent high quality product, but also in response to the more frequent occurrence of dry growing seasons in recent years. Although the quantity used for irrigation is relatively small in total, it tends to be highest in hot dry weather when water resources are most stretched. Also most of the irrigation water is lost to the atmosphere, whereas water used for most other purposes is eventually returned to rivers and can be reused.

In England and Wales, an average of 150 litres of water per person per day is used in the home (in comparison with the average of 860 litres per person per day for domestic, industrial and agricultural purposes in industrialized countries calculated in Question 7.1). Figure 1.2 showed a breakdown of this use. The domestic demand has grown from 36 litres per person per day at about the time of the last major cholera epidemic in London (1858) to 150 litres today because of improved living standards. Nearly all (over 99%) homes in England and Wales are now linked to the public water supply. Similar patterns of water use exist in other industrialized nations.

Activity 7.1

How does your water use compare with that in Figure 1.2? In this Activity you will measure how much water you use in one of these categories, that of a bath or shower.

Over a period of a week, keep a record of how many baths and/or showers you have, and the duration of each shower. Work out how much water you use in an average bath, by measuring how long your bath tap takes to fill a measuring jug or kettle, and how long the bath takes to run. Do the same for a shower, measuring how long it takes to fill the jug or kettle, so you can calculate the amount of water use per minute of shower (as in Table 1.2).

Calculate your weekly water use for a bath or shower, and finally your daily use averaged over a week. How does it compare with the data in Figure 1.2, assuming an average domestic use of 150 litres per person per day?

7.2   Prediction of demand

For a major water supply project there is a substantial time between the recognition of the need for water and the completion of the project (the lead time), so predictions of the future demand for water are essential and need to be made for around 25 years ahead. Prediction starts by looking at how the demand for water has varied in the past. Figure 7.2 shows how abstractions varied between 1971 and 2001 in England and Wales. Although there is little difference in total abstractions for 1971 and 2001, there were large variations during this period, with a maximum of around $45 \times 10^6 \, m^3$ per day in 1992, and a minimum of around $32 \times 10^6 \, m^3$ per day in 1994.

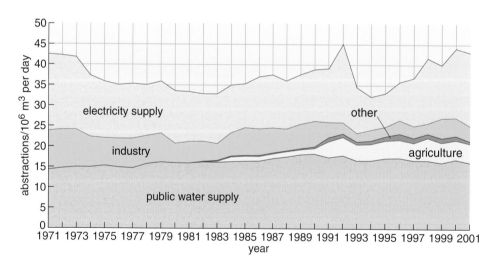

Figure 7.2   Abstractions from non-tidal surface water and groundwater by use in England and Wales, 1971–2001 (DEFRA, 2004). *Note*: data collected before 1991 are not strictly comparable with later years. The abstraction for each use is given by the vertical spacing between the lines, e.g. electricity supply in 1971 abstracted $42.5 - 23.5 \times 10^6 \, m^3$ per day $= 19 \times 10^6 \, m^3$ per day. The total abstraction is given by the top line.

● Which use in Figure 7.2 has had the least variation between 1971 and 2001?

○ The public water supply, which varied only between around $14.5 \times 10^6 \, m^3$ per day in 1971 to around $17.5 \times 10^6 \, m^3$ per day in 1990.

The other uses have much greater variability; agriculture, for example, has increased from very little before 1983 to around $5 \times 10^6 \, m^3$ per day from 1992.

● The variation in which use has had the greatest effect on total abstractions?

◐ The electricity supply industry; for example, between 1992 and 1994, the amount of water it used dropped by about $9 \times 10^6 \, m^3$ per day.

Comparable data by use do not exist for other parts of the UK, but there are data for the public water supply (Table 7.2).

● What was the general trend in the amount of water used by the public water supply in the UK between 1990 and 2002?

◐ It has generally decreased, from over $20 \times 10^6 \, m^3$ per day in 1990/1 to around $18.5 \times 10^6 \, m^3$ per day in 2001/2. However, the decrease is not regular; there are yearly increases, particularly in 1994/5 and 1995/6.

Table 7.2   Public water supply in the UK: 1990/1–2001/2, in $10^6 \, m^3$ per day. (DEFRA, 2004)

	1990/1	1991/2	1992/3	1993/4	1994/5	1995/6	1997/8	1998/9	1999/2000	2000/1	2001/2
England and Wales	17.38	17.20	16.76	16.76	17.11	17.32	15.98	15.34	15.33	15.26	15.78
Scotland	2.30	2.24	2.21	2.27	2.26	2.32	2.34	2.33	2.44	2.40	2.02
Northern Ireland	0.68	0.68	0.67	0.67	0.69	0.70	0.69	0.69	0.70	0.72	0.74
United Kingdom	20.36	20.12	19.64	19.70	20.06	20.34	19.01	18.36	18.47	18.38	18.54

Box 7.1   Water metering

With a water meter (Figure 7.3), a household, office or industry pays for the water it actually uses instead of paying a fixed charge unrelated to use. Most homes in Europe and North America have water meters but in England and Wales, although almost all new homes are installed with water meters, in total only 24% of homes are metered (2003). This is generally higher in areas of water stress, for example, the Anglian water company region meters about a half of its domestic customers. Offices and industry are usually metered.

The advantage of metering is that it tends to reduce demand as it raises awareness and encourages consumers to consider and value their use of water. In the long term, it has led to changes in attitude to water, so that more people are choosing devices that are water efficient. This encourages manufacturers to make and advertise water-efficient household appliances, such as WC cisterns, washing machines and dishwashers.

The disadvantages are the cost of metering and a concern about health. Installing meters in existing homes costs about £130–£200 per home, an enormous investment across the country. There is also a concern on health grounds that some households will sacrifice cleanliness in order to economize.

The EA long-term strategy for water resources in England and Wales (EA, 2001) is that 50 to 75% of households should be metered by 2025.

Figure 7.3   With a water meter, a customer is charged for the volume of water used.

Public water supplies in England and Wales generally increased between 1971 and 1990 (Figure 7.2). Domestic consumption rose during this period due to population growth and the increasing domestic use of water per person. The fall since 1990 (Table 7.2) is due to domestic metering, more efficient use of industrial water, periods of industrial recession, and reduced leakage. The metered water supply in England and Wales rose gradually through the 1990s, and the unmetered supply fell, partly due to the increase in domestic metering.

Graphs such as Figure 7.2 have to be projected far into the future because of the long lead times necessary in planning for new water resources. As well as looking at past trends, prediction of the future demand for water involves breaking down the total present demand into domestic, industrial and agricultural components, and identifying the economic, social and population factors which are likely to affect each of them in the future.

Forecasts include assumptions about increases in domestic demand due to greater use of appliances such as automatic washing machines and waste-disposal units, and decreases in domestic demand due to more showers and fewer baths, dual-flush WCs, and water metering to houses. They also include assumptions about population growth, the level of economic activity, climate change (Section 7.4) and the rate of leakage from the system (Box 7.2).

The assumptions that have to be made to predict demand reveal the uncertainties inherent in forecasting, and the forecasts may turn out to be highly inaccurate (Table 7.3). This can be seen easily in retrospect: for example, the 1971 England and Wales forecast for 1981 was $19.2 \times 10^6 \, \text{m}^3$ per day, whereas the real demand was much less — about $15.9 \times 10^6 \, \text{m}^3$ per day. The 1973 estimate for the year 2000 of $28 \times 10^6 \, \text{m}^3$ per day is now seen to be far too high. For a shorter prediction period, the 1987 forecast for 1991 was accurate, but time will tell whether its predictions for 2011 or the 1992 predictions for 2021 are any good. Judging by previous forecasts, they probably will not be. The failure in recent years to make accurate predictions of the future demand for water in the UK has been partly caused by the difficulty in predicting industrial changes. 2001 predictions are discussed in Section 7.5.

Table 7.3   Past forecasts of public water supply for England and Wales.

Year of forecast	For year	Predicted demand /$10^6 \, \text{m}^3$ per day	Water supplied /$10^6 \, \text{m}^3$ per day
1971	1981	19.2	15.9
1973	2000	28.0	15.3
1987	1991	17.0	17.3
1987	2001	18.3	15.5
1987	2011	19.5	
1992	2021	20.5	

Box 7.2   Leakage

More water is lost through leaks in the public water supply distribution system than is put to any one use. In 2002/3 the leakage in England and Wales was estimated as $3.6 \times 10^6 \, \text{m}^3$ per day, around 22% of the water put into the system. The leakage rate is greater in cities, where water mains date back to Victorian times, most of which are now dilapidated. Here leakage can reach 40%. However 'lost' is a relative term, as much of the water that leaks from the mains recharges aquifers.

Water is lost through continual gradual leakage, as well as from spectacular temporary bursts caused by vibration, soil compaction, corrosion or excavation when installing gas pipes and electricity and telephone cables (Figure 7.4). There are around 20 bursts per year in England and Wales for every 100 km of water mains — and there are over 3×10^5 km of mains.

Leakage can be, and is being, reduced by replacing or relining old mains, but it is both very expensive and very disruptive, involving digging up roads and tunnelling under buildings. Mandatory leakage control targets were introduced during the 1990s in England and Wales. This reduced a leakage of around $5.1 \times 10^6 \, \text{m}^3$ per day in 1994/5 (about 31%) to $3.6 \times 10^6 \, \text{m}^3$ per day (22%) in 2002/3. Leakage reduction at present (2004) is planned to be 1.5% a year. The Thames water company, which has many Victorian mains in the London area, managed to reduce its leakage from $1.1 \times 10^6 \, \text{m}^3$ per day in 1995/6 to $0.77 \times 10^6 \, \text{m}^3$ per day in 1998/9. However, despite continuing mains replacement, in 2002/3 this had risen to $0.93 \times 10^6 \, \text{m}^3$ per day, a leakage of 33%.

As well as being slow, there is also a technical and economic limit for leakage reduction. The aim is to reach an economic level of leakage, which is the point at which the cost of reducing leakage is the same as the value of the water saved. This point is not fixed because of improving technology in locating leaks and changes in the price of water.

Figure 7.4   A burst water main is great fun to play in, but is very disruptive and a waste of water.

7.3   Reducing demand

Water, at an average cost to the consumer in England and Wales in 2004 of £0.80 per m^3 (0.08p per litre) for supply, has always been cheap compared with other familiar liquids such as milk, petrol or bottled water (all about 60–90p per litre). If you used tap water at the average rate of 150 litres a day and had a pint of milk a day, the annual cost would be about £37 for your water but around £110 for your milk (2004). As well as being cheap, water is also convenient (the only liquid piped to most homes) and there is usually no limit on its use. Not all countries use as much water per head as the UK; in countries where the rainfall is less or is seasonal, water will be either more expensive or rationed unless the country is prosperous, and in extreme cases water is available in such limited quantities that shortage of water is a major factor limiting the economic growth of a country.

People in England and Wales began to be more aware of water supply problems in the 1970s, when water authorities began to collect water rates separately from general rates; this made the domestic consumer really aware of the cost of water for the first time. The point that water supplies are not unlimited was made forcibly by the 1975–76 drought, when rationing by standpipes and cutoff periods had to be introduced in England and Wales (Box 7.3).

Box 7.3 Drought in England and Wales

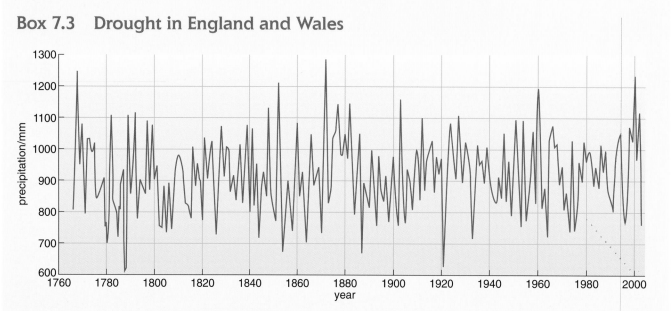

Figure 7.5   Annual precipitation in England and Wales 1766–2003.

A **drought** is when there is insufficient rainfall to maintain adequate water levels in rivers, reservoirs and aquifers. This places stress on water resources and the environment. England and Wales had droughts in 1975–76, 1984, 1988–92, and 1995–97.

Figure 7.5 shows the annual precipitation in England and Wales for 1766–2003. This varies between extremes of about 600 mm and about 1300 mm. There are also longer term drier periods (e.g. 1895–1907) and wetter periods (e.g. the 1870s).

Is low annual precipitation the cause of droughts? Table 7.4 gives the annual precipitation in England and Wales for 1990–2002. The 1990 and 1991 precipitation values are less than the long-term average and so are the values for 1995, 1996 and 1997. These years of low precipitation are the same

as the drought years noted above, so there is a relationship. But drought also depends on temperature, time of year and the water sources used for supply in a particular area.

Figure 7.6 gives rainfall plotted against temperature in England and Wales, for winter and summer periods. The plots for the more recent years, 1974–2003, show a tendency for warmer, wetter winters and hotter, drier summers in comparison with earlier times.

● What are the characteristics of 1995 on Figure 7.6?

◔ 1995 has the equal lowest summer rainfall (150 mm less than the mean), but a high winter precipitation (170 mm higher than the mean). However, it is 2 °C warmer in both summer and winter.

Table 7.4   Annual precipitation for 1990–2002 in England and Wales, in mm, and as a percentage of the long-term average (LTA) of 1961–1990 (895 mm). (DEFRA, 2004)

	1990	1991	1992	1993	1994	1995	1996	1997	1998	1999	2000	2001	2002
Annual rainfall/mm	838	790	949	983	1023	830	755	864	1057	1004	1176	912	1069
% LTA	94	88	106	110	114	93	84	97	118	112	131	102	119

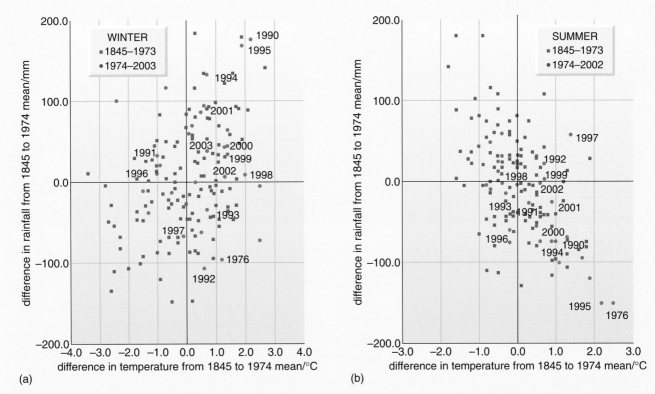

(a)

(b)

Figure 7.6   Average precipitation and temperature in England and Wales, for (a) winter (December to February 1845–2003; year label is for the end of winter) and (b) summer (June to August 1845–2002) periods. These are scatter plots of differences from the 1845–1974 means. The plots for most recent years, 1974–2003, are red dots and selected years are labelled.

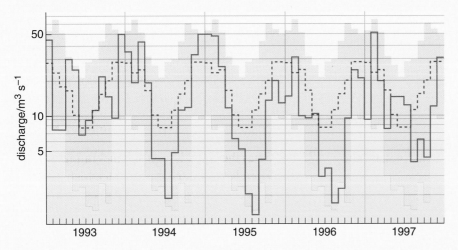

Figure 7.7   A hydrograph (blue line) for the River South Tyne, in north-east England, 1993–1997. The long-term maximum (top of pale blue area), minimum (bottom of pale blue area) and mean flows (red dashes) are also shown. The discharge scale is non-linear.

Times of low summer rainfall and high temperatures can produce 'summer droughts' which hit areas mainly supplied from surface water sources. This occurred in 1984, 1989 and 1995. A succession of winters with low precipitation, and reduced aquifer recharge, will produce longer-term drought as in 1988–92 and 1995–97.

Do river discharge and groundwater level data also indicate past droughts? The River South Tyne (Figure 7.7) had discharges lower than the mean for most months between the spring of 1995 and the autumn of 1997. These were drought years, so there can be a relationship between discharge and drought.

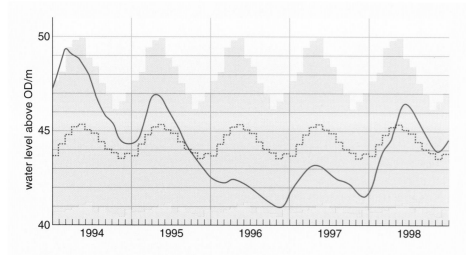

Figure 7.8 Mean monthly water level for 1994–98 (blue line) in an observation well at Washpit Farm in Norfolk. The long-term (1950–97) maximum (top of pale blue area), minimum (bottom of pale blue area) and mean values (red dashes) are also shown.

Groundwater level can also be a drought indicator. Figure 7.8 gives the groundwater level for a well in Norfolk. The low summer rainfall in 1995 caused the water table to fall. Most of the rain in the following winter was absorbed by the moisture-deficient soil, and very little infiltrated to recharge the underlying aquifers. 1996 and 1997 continued to have a low rainfall (Table 7.4) and it was not until the higher than average rainfall of 1998 that the water table rose to normal levels. However, it is worth remembering that because of the very large volume of water stored in aquifers, groundwater is resilient to droughts in comparison with surface water. The problem is that there are not enough wells to extract the water and those that are available are often overpumped in droughts and may fail. Over-extracting groundwater may also reduce baseflow to rivers.

7.4 Changing climate

The climate is believed to be changing as a result of increased emissions of some gases to the atmosphere by human activities, especially by our use of fossil fuels. The UK Climate Impacts Programme (UKCIP) has identified that mean annual temperatures in the UK have increased by about 0.7 °C over the last 300 years, with most of this, about 0.5 °C of warming, occurring during the 20th century. This warming is predicted to continue throughout the 21st century.

Detailed prediction of climatic change is difficult, because of the natural variability of the climate, which may magnify or reduce the effect of climate change on a shorter timescale. Some events that we have been experiencing recently (droughts and floods) may be part of the natural variability, or extremes caused by the changing climate.

Planning for future water resources in the UK has to take into account climatic changes. Current (2004) climatic change predictions by UKCIP suggest that:

- the average annual temperature across the UK will rise by between 2 °C and 3.5 °C by 2080;

- the warming will be greater in the south and east of the UK;

- winters will become wetter and summers will become drier, though even by the 2020s, changes will still be within the range of the natural variations we experience now;

- the annual variability of rainfall will increase — there will be both more wet years and more dry years.

Climate change affects planning for water resources in three ways.

- *Demand for water*   Domestic water use is likely to increase due to hotter summers, mainly due to increased washing and garden watering. The total impact on industrial water use is uncertain; some uses will increase (e.g. water cooling is less efficient at higher temperatures so the demand may increase) and some will decrease. Agricultural water demand will increase (e.g. for greater irrigation and more drinking water for livestock).

- *Availability of water*   Higher winter rainfall will increase river discharge, reservoir replenishment and aquifer recharge in winter, but summer discharges and infiltration will decrease, particularly in the south and east. Water availability will therefore become less reliable. Evaporation will increase due to higher temperatures.

- *Environmental impact*   Changes in river discharge and groundwater levels will have an impact on the plants and animals that rely on the water environment; some will thrive under the changed conditions and some will find it hard to survive. Designated conservation areas will need protection by reducing abstractions to maintain summer flows and groundwater levels (Figure 7.9).

Figure 7.9   Freshwater wetlands such as this in the Somerset Levels may be at risk from changes in water availability caused by climate change.

7.5   Future supply

The UK as a whole has more water than it is ever likely to need but much of the water is in the *wrong place*: areas with the greatest resources are not the areas of highest demand.

Scotland has sufficient water resources for all foreseeable circumstances and has not experienced droughts. An enormous amount of additional water could be made available by reservoir storage in the Highlands. But nowadays there is a trend towards more flexible schemes. In many of these schemes, rivers are regulated by upland reservoirs, and water is abstracted from rivers and lochs in the areas of demand in the lowlands; in others, water supply is developed in conjunction with hydroelectric power generation.

Northern Ireland also has sufficient water resources, most of the supply being provided by surface water sources. Much of the existing storage is in small upland reservoirs, although Lough Neagh, with an area of 385 km^2, has become a major source of water for Belfast. Abstraction from Lough Neagh could be greatly increased to meet future increases in demand.

Wales has a considerable amount of water; but much of it is heavily committed to Welsh needs, or to the needs of the north-west and the west Midlands in England. However, there is the potential in Wales for more storage of water if necessary.

England has areas with a surplus of water, such as the north-east, and areas of water deficiency, mainly in the south-east, where part of the supply depends on transfer from other areas. We have seen that in England and Wales the total amount of water abstracted has generally increased since 1993 (Figure 7.2). To understand how this demand could continue to be met in the future we need to look at the water supplies by region (Table 7.5). Question 7.2 will help you become familiar with these regional differences.

Table 7.5   Estimated water abstractions in 2001 (public water supply and total abstractions) for EA regions in England and Wales. The values are not the same as in Figure 7.2, as the values in the table include brackish water.

EA region	Public water supply /10^6 m^3 per day		Total abstractions /10^6 m^3 per day	
	surface	ground	surface	ground
Anglian	1.316	0.759	4.011	1.000
North East	1.875	0.318	5.813	0.482
North West	1.342	0.109	9.773	0.268
Midlands	1.773	0.869	5.618	1.224
Southern	0.345	1.039	5.141	1.379
South West	0.728	0.488	7.681	0.726
Thames	2.802	1.315	4.635	1.498
Wales	1.926	0.048	10.651	0.088
Total	12.107	4.945	53.323	6.665

(handwritten notes in right margin: 36.6, 14.5, 7.5, 22.9, 75.1, 40.1, 31.9, 2.43, 29.)

Question 7.2

(a) Which region abstracts the greatest total quantity of water, and why?

(b) Which region abstracts the greatest amount of water for public water supply?

(c) Which three regions get the greatest *proportion* of their public water supply from groundwater, and which region the least?

(handwritten notes in right margin: Wales; Thames; Southern (75%), Anglian (36.6%), South W (40.1), Wales)

The rocks of the Wales and North West regions are mainly Cambrian to Carboniferous in age. These old rocks have been compacted, folded and in many cases subjected to metamorphism. They are relatively impermeable and make poor aquifers. The rocks in the Southern and Thames regions are younger — Cretaceous and Tertiary — and are only very gently folded. They are mainly sedimentary rocks, of which the Chalk and sands make good aquifers. The rocks in Scotland and Northern Ireland are mainly older igneous and metamorphic rocks, which make poor aquifers.

The distribution of the principal aquifers in the UK is shown in Figure 7.10. The three main aquifers are the Cretaceous Chalk (which supplies more than half of the groundwater in England and Wales, as it underlies large areas of south and east England where the demand is high), Permian and Triassic sandstones, and Jurassic limestones. Other aquifers are Carboniferous limestones and sandstones, Permian limestones, Cretaceous sands and Quaternary sands and gravels.

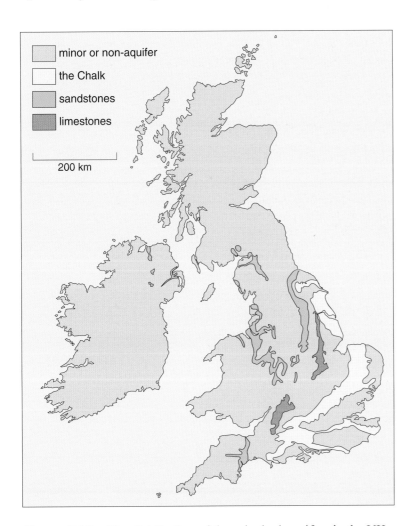

minor or non-aquifer

the Chalk

sandstones

limestones

200 km

Figure 7.10 The distribution of the principal aquifers in the UK.

The areas where there are surpluses of water resources over demand in England and Wales for 2001 are shown in Figures 7.11a, b and c.

● Which areas have additional surface water available in winter and which in summer?

○ Much of England and Wales, except for the south-east, has additional water available in winter. However, in the summer there are few areas with spare water, mainly parts of west Wales and north-east England.

● Does groundwater availability follow the same regional pattern of spare surface water?

○ Not in detail, there is additional groundwater available in small parts of most regions of England and Wales except for the south-west. Although the precipitation is less in the south and east, those areas have major aquifers.

The areas most at risk of future shortages are the Anglian, Thames and Southern regions, areas with low surpluses and depending heavily on groundwater supplies (Table 7.5). If groundwater is not recharged sufficiently in winter, as happened in the winters of 1995 and 1996 (Figure 7.8) this may leave insufficient groundwater for extraction during the summer, and may reduce river discharge by a reduction of baseflow.

However, some areas have more water than they need at present. The completion of the Kielder reservoir in the NE region in 1980 doubled the amount of water available to the region, but this water has not been fully used — the demand has risen less than was predicted when it was built and the region now has surplus water (Figures 7.11a and b). Kielder was built to increase the supply to industry in the north-east, such as British Steel and ICI, who expected big increases in demand. Instead, industrial output has declined and their need for water has fallen since 1980.

Although north-west England (and Scotland) have higher precipitation than the south-east, they have relatively little storage (few aquifers, and reservoirs hold relatively small amounts of water). The precipitation gradient runs one way, the storage gradient the other. So when there is a severe drought over the whole of the UK, the north-west or west often gets into trouble before the south-east. There have not been standpipes or rota cuts in the south-east since 1970, but there have been in Devon and South Wales (1976).

Most of the growth in demand at present, and predicted in the future, is in south and east England. This is a major problem, as these are also the regions of shortage and are vulnerable to drought. Water shortages in these areas are already causing environmental problems such as reductions in river flow and even drying up of some rivers in dry summers. Tackling the river problem would mean reducing abstraction — and increasing shortages.

In 2001 the EA published its strategy for water resources up to 2025 in England and Wales (EA, 2001). The EA stated that its vision was:

'Abstraction of water that is environmentally and economically sustainable, providing the right amount for people, agriculture, commerce and industry, and an improved water-related environment'.

Figure 7.11 (a) Availability of winter surface water in England and Wales, 2001. The regions outlined here are the eight EA regions. (b) Availability of summer surface water in England and Wales, 2001. (c) Availability of groundwater in England and Wales, 2001.

Legend:
- Unsustainable or unacceptable abstraction regime
- No additional water available
- Additional water available
- No strategic aquifers

200 km

The EA strategy recognized that:

- in much of England and Wales, water is a scarce resource
- the public water supply provision should be increased by $1.1 \times 10^6 \, \text{m}^3$ per day
- efficient use of water is essential
- leakage should be reduced.

Agriculture should use available water to the best effect, as in many agricultural areas little further summer water is available. This will involve increased winter storage of water and a change in crops.

As part of the strategy, the EA had to predict future changes in water use and demand. The forecasts were based on the Department of Trade and Industry's 'Foresight' programme, which has scenarios defining a broad framework of possible social, political and technological change. The EA developed four different scenarios, each considering variations in demand by household, leakage, industry and commerce, and irrigation. The effects of climatic change predictions were also taken into account. Scenario alpha, for example, included increasing household demand, weak leakage control and increased irrigation. Scenario delta was for reduced household demand, leakage reduction, low economic growth and lower irrigation use (Figure 7.12).

The scenarios show that demand for water is highly dependent on societal choice and governance. The general demand for water rises in two of the scenarios, and falls in the other two. Changes are driven by economic pressures, people's desire to see water used in different ways, and technological changes. The EA recommended that the extra water needed for public water supply in scenarios alpha and beta should come from a combination of resource development and demand management; this reflects a change from *demand led* to *demand managed* water supply. They proposed resource development of around $1.8 \times 10^6 \, \text{m}^3$ per day, providing $1.1 \times 10^6 \, \text{m}^3$ per day for the public water supply (Figure 7.12) and the rest for environmental improvements. The strategy includes the water companies spending £5.3 billion nationally on environmental projects to

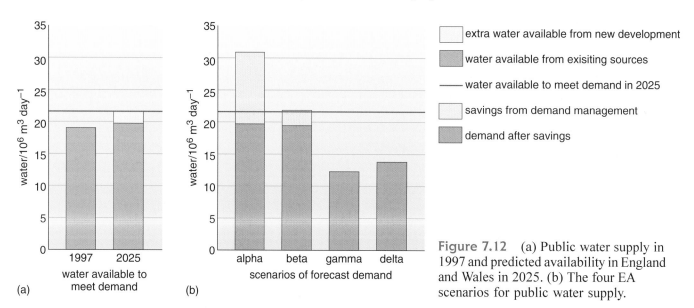

Figure 7.12 (a) Public water supply in 1997 and predicted availability in England and Wales in 2025. (b) The four EA scenarios for public water supply.

improve rivers and coastal waters up to 2005, and £400 million improving water resources related sites, which will protect important wildlife sites. For example, the East Devon Pebblebed Heaths have wetlands which support the rare southern damselfly and other species. South West Water owns two intakes that abstract water from critical parts of the site, which could affect water levels. The company, after discussion with the EA and English Nature, shut down the intakes in 2003.

Most of the EA recommendations for enhancing water resources involve making the most of existing schemes — the inflexible and environmentally destructive days of immediately commissioning new reservoirs seem to be over. The strategy generally recommends:

- increasing winter storage (making use of the wetter winters of climate change predictions), by enlarging existing reservoirs in the south and east, increased conjunctive use in the north-east, and a possible new reservoir in the Thames catchment
- inter-regional transfers, such as the possibility of a Severn–Thames transfer
- utilizing rising groundwater in London and Birmingham
- greater re-use of sewage effluent.

Scenarios and strategies have been developed on a regional basis as well as nationally, with targets for regional resource developments and demand management. All regions have identified some resource developments, water savings targets and environmental improvements, but the proportion varies with the situation and need: most of the growth in demand is in the south and east. The Thames region, for example, has a target for resource development of $0.59 \times 10^6 \, \text{m}^3$ per day, and water savings of $0.75 \times 10^6 \, \text{m}^3$ per day, whereas the North West region has a target for resource development of $0.035 \times 10^6 \, \text{m}^3$ per day, and water savings of $0.016 \times 10^6 \, \text{m}^3$ per day.

7.6 Summary of Chapter 7

1   The lead times for water resources projects are quite long (they can be about 25 years) so estimates of the future demand for water must be made for at least this time ahead.

2   Prediction of the future demand for water starts by looking at how demand has varied in the past. It involves breaking down the total demand into domestic, industrial and agricultural components, and identifying the economic, social, population and climate change factors which are likely to affect them in the future. Past predictions have not been accurate, especially in the long term.

3   Most domestic consumers have little direct incentive to economize on water use, as only 24% of homes in England and Wales have water meters (2003). The water supply to industry is metered, so in that sector there is a financial inducement to economize on water use. 22% (2002/3) of the water put into the distribution system in England and Wales is lost by leakage, but it is very expensive, time consuming and disruptive to remedy.

4   The UK as a whole has more water than it needs, but much of it is in the wrong place. Scotland, Northern Ireland and Wales have sufficient water resources, although part of the water in Wales is diverted for use in England.

England has areas of both water surplus and water shortage. Groundwater is a large proportion of the public water supply in the southern and eastern parts of England. It forms only a small proportion in other parts of England and in Wales, Scotland and Northern Ireland, as the rocks in these areas are mainly older sedimentary, igneous or metamorphic rocks, and so are not good aquifers.

5   The EA outlined a strategy in 2001 for water resources up to 2025. This involves resource development, demand management and environmental improvement. Resource development would concentrate on increasing winter storage, by enlarging existing reservoirs, increased conjunctive use, a possible new reservoir in the Thames catchment, inter-regional transfers, utilization of rising groundwater in London and Birmingham and greater re-use of sewage effluent.

6   The area of the UK likely to have the greatest problems with water supply in the future is the south and east of England.

GLOBAL WATER RESOURCES

The amount of water used on a global scale has increased rapidly in recent years. Increased demand is due to population growth and increased per capita consumption of water. The rate of increase in industrialized countries is the lowest; most of the increase is in the developing world, which has a much lower per capita water use at present. 70% of global water use is for agriculture, 22% for industry and 8% for domestic purposes (Table 1.1). This division has a considerable regional variation: in Africa, India and Asia, agriculture is even more water-demanding, with Asia, for example, using 85% for agriculture (Figure 8.1). In Europe and the USA, industry uses a greater proportion: 55% and 49%, respectively.

Water, however, is a resource in which 'used' is a relative term: some agricultural water and most industrial and domestic water is returned to rivers or groundwater after use, but usually with a change of quality. And, we have seen that rivers themselves have a residence time of only a few weeks (Section 2.1), so the water in them is renewed on a very short timescale.

On a global scale, water is not scarce, but locally on a continental or national scale it often is (Figure 8.1), and with increasing demand is likely to be more so in the future. In 2000, 5% of the global population was estimated to be *water scarce*, meaning less than 1000 m³ of fresh water was available per person per

Figure 8.1 Global water use and distribution. The bar charts show percentage use by category.

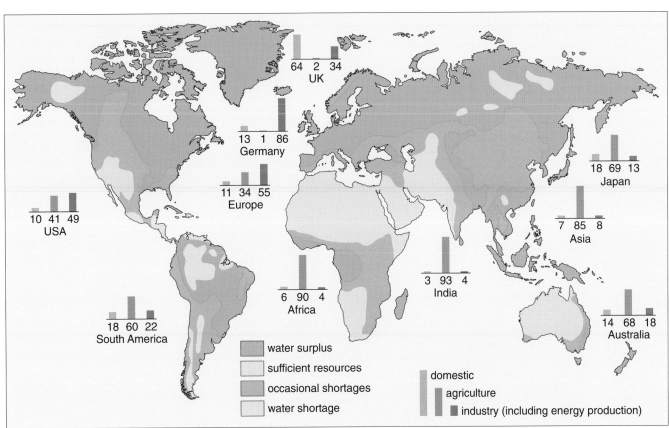

year; by 2025 this is estimated to affect 31% of the population. Many of these people are in countries with high population growth rates and their water problems are increasing rapidly.

The water-scarce countries also have another water problem apart from scarcity — the water is often unsafe to drink. Every year, over 2 million people die from water-borne diseases. So having sufficient water is not enough; it must be unpolluted water. Access to safe water varies with region (Table 8.1), being lowest in Africa. The access in cities, about 94%, is much higher than in rural areas, where it is only about 71%. Globally, 18% of the population lack access to safe drinking water — and that is over 1 billion people. Lack of safe water is due both to lack of investment in water supply systems and to inadequate maintenance of the systems. About a half of the water in supply systems in the developing world is lost to leakage, illegal abstractions and vandalism. In some countries, water is highly subsidized for those connected to the system, while poorer people not connected rely on unsafe sources or expensive private sellers. Globally, 2.4 billion people lack access to adequate sanitation. In developing countries over 90% of sewage is dumped untreated into waters where the water supplies can be polluted. Recognizing these problems, the World Summit on Sustainable Development in Johannesburg in 2002 set water targets to address these issues (Table 8.2).

Table 8.1   Access to water supply and sanitation. (Data are for 1999.)

Region	Population/millions	Percentage of population with access to:	
		water supply	sanitation
Africa	784	62	60
Asia	3682	81	48
Europe	728	96	92
Latin America and the Caribbean	519	83	76
North America	309	100	100
Oceania	30	87	93
Total	6052	82	60

Table 8.2   The water targets of the World Summit on Sustainable Development 2002.

The four water targets	Current state of affairs
Halve the proportion of people without access to adequate sanitation by 2021	2.4 billion people don't have access to sanitation
Prioritize programmes of action to reach the sanitation and water targets	2.2 million people die each year of water-related diseases
Develop plans for integrated water management by 2005	
Invest in water initiatives	

Even in parts of the world where there is little or no scarcity of water, environmental side-effects of water use are often becoming of great concern. This includes not only the obvious pollution, particularly of sewage, nitrates and high TDS, but also the destruction of natural wetland habitats by diversion of water elsewhere, falling water tables due to over-extraction, and the drowning of land by enormous reservoirs. About half of the rivers and lakes in Europe and North America are still seriously polluted, despite improvements in recent years. Water quality may be the biggest emerging water problem for the industrialized world.

Water shortages have caused major international disputes in many parts of the world (Table 8.3). Water management is particularly difficult in areas where the catchment of a river crosses many countries. Egypt, for example, gets most of its water from the River Nile, whose flow originates mainly from seven upstream countries. In the Middle East, water resources are of strategic concern, and a major cause of political conflict. Full-scale water wars are unlikely, but tension between countries competing for water is escalating to the extent that in some areas war has been threatened (Box 8.1). The following quotes illustrate points of view on water disputes:

Attributed to Mark Twain:

'Whisky's for drinkin', water's for fightin' '

A considered view from a country involved in water disputes, from an Israeli Defence Forces analyst (Wolf, 1999):

'Why go to war over water? For the price of one week's fighting, you could build five desalination plants. No loss of life, no international pressure, and a reliable supply you don't have to defend in hostile territory.'

Table 8.3 International water disputes.

Rivers/aquifers	Countries involved in dispute	Subject of dispute
Nile	Egypt, Sudan, Ethiopia, Uganda, Kenya, Democratic Republic of Congo, Eritrea	siltation, flooding, water flow/diversion
Euphrates, Tigris	Iraq, Syria, Turkey	dams, reduced water flow, salinization, hydroelectricity
Jordan, Yarmouk, Litani, West Bank aquifers	Israel, Jordan, Syria, Lebanon, Palestinians on the West Bank	water flow/diversion, allotment of water from common aquifers
Brahmaputra, Ganges	Bangladesh, India	siltation, flooding, water flow/diversion
Mekong	Kampuchea, Laos, Thailand, Vietnam	water flow, flooding, irrigation
Parana	Argentina, Brazil	dam, land inundation
Lauca	Bolivia, Chile	dam, salinization
Rio Grande, Colorado	Mexico, United States	salinization, water flow, agrochemical pollution
Great Lakes	Canada, United States	water diversion
Rhine	France, Netherlands, Switzerland, Germany	industrial pollution
Danube	Austria, Slovakia, Hungary	water diversion, hydroelectricity

Box 8.1   Water in the Middle East

The Middle East is an area of low precipitation and high evapotranspiration, much of it with less than 200 mm precipitation a year and potential evapotranspiration of over 2000 mm; this defines it as 'arid'. It has a few rivers, arising in the mountains, two of which, the Euphrates and Tigris, are a major source of water in the region (Figure 8.2). Another river, the Jordan and its tributaries, is of significance to the west of the region. The limited water resources of the region have led to international disputes over water supplies (Table 8.3), the two main disputes being between Israel and its neighbours, and between Iraq, Syria and Turkey over the Euphrates and Tigris rivers.

Many of the countries in the Middle East are water-scarce; Israel for example has about 300 m^3 of fresh water available per person per year and Kuwait about 1 m^3 of water available per person per year. In recent years, large population increases into some areas resulting from immigration (e.g. Israel) or high birthrate have made agreement on equitable distribution of water imperative. This has been exacerbated by a series of Arab–Israeli conflicts and disputes between Arab countries.

Secure water supplies have been a primary concern for Israel ever since the creation of the state in 1948, and in the 1950s there were plans to share the waters of the Yarmouk river (a tributary of the River Jordan) and Lake Tiberias with Jordan and Syria. However, Syria objected to Israel's plans to divert water from the Jordan above Lake Tiberias and Israel objected to a Syrian scheme to dam the Yarmouk as it would reduce flow into the Jordan. The 1967 war resulted in Israeli occupation of the Golan Heights, southern Lebanon and the West Bank, which strengthened Israel's water supply position, as it controlled the headwaters of the Jordan and aquifers of the West Bank. However, drought and increased extraction during the later 20th century reduced the levels of Lake Tiberias and increased its salinity to levels that threaten its aquatic life, and increasing groundwater exploitation above the safe yield has lowered aquifer levels, causing saline intrusion into the coastal aquifer. To increase its water security, Israel is constructing desalination plants (Section 6.4). However, water continues to be a central feature of peace negotiations in this area.

The other major area of water dispute in the Middle East involves the Euphrates and Tigris rivers, which rise in the mountains of Turkey and flow southwards into Syria and Iraq, dependent on these rivers for most of their water supply. Turkey, as the upstream country, claims the right to control the water that originates within its border. Iraq claims historical rights to the rivers as its people have depended on them for thousands of years, in what was Mesopotamia, using them for large-scale irrigation. Syria claims both ownership rights and historical user rights. Unfortunately there is just not enough water for all the counties, leading to conflict and, at times, threats of war.

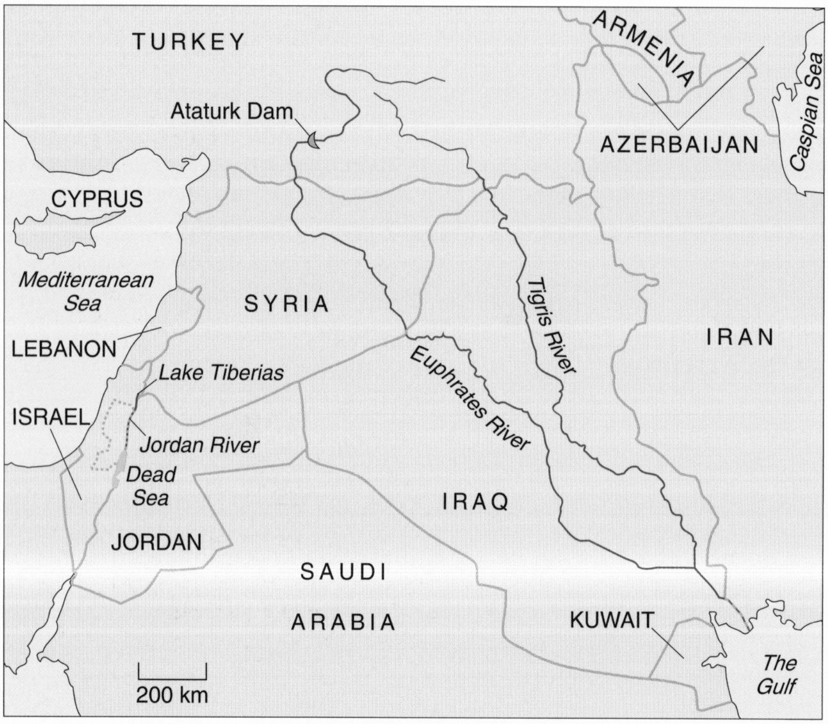

Figure 8.2   The Middle East, with major rivers: the Jordan, Euphrates and Tigris.

Figure 8.3   These two false-colour satellite images show the enormous size of the lake created by the Ataturk Dam (bottom left) in Turkey on the River Euphrates. This is one of the largest dams in the region, completed in 1990. The images show an area about 175 × 175 km. (a) in 1983, before the dam was built, and (b) in 2002, after the lake had filled. The red areas indicate vegetation.

In 1974 Syria cut off the flow of the Euphrates to Iraq in order to fill a new reservoir. Iraq assembled troops on the Syrian border and threatened invasion, with the result that Syria hastily released water back into the river. In 1990, Turkey stopped the flow of the Euphrates to fill the reservoir behind the Ataturk Dam (Figure 8.3); Syria and Iraq insisted that Turkey restore the flow, which it did, but a month later. Greater cooperation between the three countries to manage the rivers on a catchment scale, and changes to agricultural practice will be necessary to manage the water resources of these major rivers effectively, but there are many obstacles to this, especially as water issues have a political role in the area.

Kuwait, with its extreme water scarcity, is one of the Middle Eastern countries with a different approach. There is no water shortage in Kuwait; it does not depend on rain to provide its fresh water, it depends on desalination. This requires large amounts of energy (Section 6.4); but Kuwait also has huge energy resources. Although desalination is expensive, it is definitely not out of reach for an oil-rich state in the Gulf. It shows clearly that sufficient water can be obtained — if the country can pay for it. Poverty is the villain that often forms the root

problem, not the environment or resource limitations. An economically rich country (e.g. the Gulf states) or one which can adapt (e.g. Israel) has greater water security (Figure 8.4).

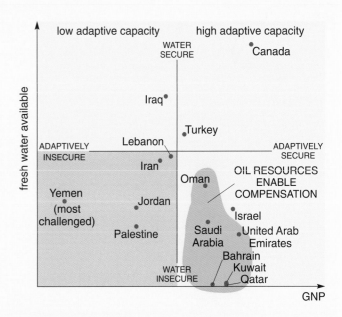

Figure 8.4   Water security in the Middle East, in relation to fresh water availability, economy (measured by gross national product, GNP) and adaptive capacity.

Water has been previously undervalued as a resource, although that is now changing — it has been called the 'blue gold' of the 21st century. Managing demand through conservation and appropriate use, rather than continuously striving to meet greater demands, is beginning to be recognized as the most environmentally sound solution.

8.1 Summary of Chapter 8

1   Globally, water use has increased rapidly in recent years due to population growth and increased per capita consumption. Most of the increase is in the developing countries. 70% of water use is for agriculture, 22% is for industry and 8% for domestic purposes, although there is considerable regional variation.

2   Water is not scarce globally, but it often is on a continental or national scale. It is estimated that 31% of the global population will live in a water-scarce country (having less than 1000 m^3 of fresh water per person per year) by 2025.

3   Water is often unsafe to drink because of pollution. This varies with continent and locally between cities and rural environments.

4   Water shortages have been the cause of major international disputes, particularly in the Middle East.

LEARNING OUTCOMES

When you have completed this book, you should be able to explain in your own words, and use correctly, all the **bold** terms printed in the text and defined in the Glossary. You should also be able, among other things, to do the following:

Chapter 1

1.1 Describe the different ways in which water is used, and the quantities used for various purposes.

1.2 Distinguish consumptive and non-consumptive uses of water.

1.3 Recognize uses of water that are elastic in demand and those uses that are inelastic in demand.

Chapter 2

2.1 Describe and quantify the processes that transfer water between parts of the hydrological cycle, calculate residence times for water in different parts of the hydrosphere, and identify those parts of the cycle that are most suitable for water resources.

2.2 Recognize the factors that control precipitation, interception, evaporation, transpiration and how these vary globally.

Chapter 3

3.1 Using information from wells, the topography of the ground and a water table contour map, carry out the following: interpret cross-sections, calculate the thickness of the unsaturated zone, and the rate of groundwater flow; deduce the direction in which groundwater is flowing; and estimate the depth to the saline interface in a coastal area from the height of the water table.

3.2 List the types of rock that usually make good aquifers, and assess how good an aquifer a rock could be, given its porosity and hydraulic conductivity.

3.3 Distinguish between unconfined and confined aquifers, and recognize conditions in confined aquifers that will produce a flowing artesian well.

3.4 Using suitable data, calculate the exploitable storage, specific yield and specific retention of an aquifer.

Chapter 4

4.1 List the types of springs, and how each type relates to a different geological setting.

4.2 Use hydrographs to distinguish overland flow and interflow from baseflow, and make inferences about the climate of an area.

4.3 Expain how various changes in land use in a river catchment will change the hydrograph of a river.

4.4 Distinguish the different types of reservoir construction, and decide whether a particular area would be suitable for a reservoir, suggest the most suitable type of dam for a site, and summarize the side-effects of constructing reservoirs.

Chapter 5

5.1 Describe the chemical compositions of natural waters, and explain how and why these compositions vary.

5.2 Describe the main sources of water pollution, the main types of pollutant and how each type may be controlled. Outline the extent of water pollution in the UK and in selected global locations.

5.3 Identify the criteria for drinking water acceptability in the EU, and outline the processes used to treat water for a public water supply.

5.4 Outline how sewage may be treated before discharge to the environment.

Chapter 6

6.1 Discuss ways of extending sources of fresh water involving both the unused parts of the hydrological cycle, and new ways of using existing water sources.

Chapter 7

7.1 Describe how water is used in the UK and the organization of water supply and sewage responsibilities and legislation.

7.2 Explain how the demand for water in England and Wales has changed between 1971 and 2001, recognize the factors involved in predicting future demand including climatic change, and discuss the importance of predictions and their limitations.

7.3 Discuss variations in the amounts of water used in different parts of England and Wales, and how water might be used more effectively. Contrast the proportions of surface water and groundwater used for the public water supply in different areas in England and Wales, identify the main aquifers, list the possible schemes for increasing water supply in England and Wales, and discuss their suitability.

Chapter 8

8.1 Discuss the future of global water resources, including problems of water scarcity and water security nationally and internationally.

REFERENCES AND FURTHER SOURCES OF INFORMATION

The information in this book has been obtained from a wide range of sources, too numerous to mention. However, specific reference is made in the text to the following:

Argles, T. (2005) *Minerals: Bulk Materials for Building and Industry* (Book 2 of S278 Earth's Physical Resources: Origin, Use and Environmental Impact), The Open University, Milton Keynes.

DEFRA (2002) Achieving a better quality of life: Review of progress towards sustainable development (PB6811).

DEFRA (2004) Key facts about: Inland water quality and use. Available online from http://www.defra.gov.uk/environment/statistics/inlwater/index.htm [last accessed December 2004].

Environment Agency (2001) *Water resources for the future: A strategy for England and Wales*. Available online from http://www.environment-agency.gov.uk/commondata/acrobat/national_report_english.pdf [last accessed December 2004].

European Union (1998) Drinking Water Directive 98/83/EC. Also available from http://europa.eu.int/comm/environment/water/water-drink/index_en.html [last accessed December 2004].

Roy, A. (1999) *The Cost of Living*, Random House, Inc., New York.

Sheldon, P. (2005) *Earth's Physical Resources: An Introduction* (Book 1 of S278 Earth's Physical Resources: Origin, Use and Environmental Impact), The Open University, Milton Keynes.

The Environment Agency (EA) in England and Wales (http://www.environment-agency.gov.uk), the Scottish Environment Protection Agency (SEPA) in Scotland (http://www.sepa.org.uk) and the Environment and Heritage Service (EHS) of the Department of the Environment in Northern Ireland (http://www.ehsni.gov.uk).

Wolf, A. T. (1999) 'Water wars' and water reality, in S. Lonergan (ed.) *Environmental Change, Adaptation and Security*, Kluwer Academic, Dordrecht, Boston, pp 251–265.

World Commission on Dams (2000) *Dams and Development: A New Framework for Decision-Making*, Earthscan, London. Also available from http://www.dams.org [last accessed December 2004].

World Heath Organization (WHO) (1993) *Guidelines on Drinking Water Quality*, 2nd edition, vol. 1, Recommendations. WHO, Geneva.

ANSWERS TO QUESTIONS

Question 1.1

Domestic water supply   Most of the domestic uses are non-substitutable, such as drinking, cooking and washing. A major use that could be substitutable, although adding complexity, is the use of composting toilets rather than flushing WCs.

Irrigation and other agricultural use   Irrigation is non-substitutable and so are many other agricultural uses such as watering stock. However, the use of water for cleaning — for example, washing out milking sheds — could be substituted by the use of straw, or air or mechanical cleaning.

Industrial manufacturing   Water is used mainly for cleaning, transporting, waste disposal and cooling. Many of these uses may be substitutable by air or mechanical processes.

Cooling   Another liquid, air or gas may be used as substitutes.

Hydroelectric power generation   No substitute (apart from substituting another form of energy).

Transport   River and coastal shipping may be substituted by land transport. Marine shipping could be substituted by air transport.

Recreation   No substitute (for this type of recreation).

The major disadvantage of substituting water is the greater cost of substitutes. Water is often used not because it is the *best* washing agent, conveying agent or coolant but because it is the *cheapest* and also harmless.

Question 2.1

(a)   The annual precipitation ranges from about 280 mm (in 1915) to about 940 mm (in 1909) (Figure 2.5).

(b)   The minimum annual precipitation as a percentage of the long-term mean:

$$\text{minimum precipitation} = \frac{280\,\text{mm}}{562\,\text{mm}} \times 100\%$$
$$= 50\%$$

Question 2.2

(a)   Range (Figure 2.8):

England 55–90 mm

Scotland 78–170 mm

Wales 82–173 mm

Northern Ireland 68–118 mm

(b)   England has the lowest range, Scotland and Wales the highest.

Question 2.3

The Southern Hemisphere has more ocean than the Northern Hemisphere, and as evaporation is greatest from open water, evaporation is greater in the Southern Hemisphere.

Question 3.1

(a)   Dense vegetation increases interception, which reduces infiltration, although the effect will be offset to some extent by the dense vegetation reducing the rate of runoff and thus increasing the time for, and therefore the amount of, infiltration.

(b)   Water rapidly runs off steeply sloping land surfaces, so there is little time for significant infiltration to occur.

(c)   Tarmac, concrete and roofing surfaces are relatively impermeable, so that roads and buildings promote overland flow and reduce infiltration.

(d)   Frozen subsoil is relatively impermeable and will reduce infiltration.

Question 3.2

(a)   Apart from at the River Poulter, the water table is nearer to the surface of the ground in the northern part (Figure 3.5b), where it is less than 10 m below the surface in many places. This distance is derived by subtracting the height of the water table above sea level from the height of the land surface.

(b)   The water table slopes downwards towards the north-east (Figure 3.5a).

(c)   Undulations in the water table tend to follow undulations in the topography. The two major topographic features are the Ryton and Poulter river valleys, beneath which there are corresponding dips in the water table. A less distinct dip underlies the River Idle.

(d)   On the highest ground the water table is about 50 m below the surface.

Question 3.3

(a)   The sample in Figure 3.14a has a fairly uniform grain size, so is geologically well-sorted, whereas samples in Figures 3.14b and c have a range of grain sizes.

(b)   Porosity is greater in well-sorted sediments, because the pore spaces are not filled by smaller grains.

(c)   Rocks with rounded grains generally have a higher porosity than rocks with angular grains; for instance, example (a) has a higher porosity than example (c).

(d)   Porosity in Figures 3.14a to d are, respectively, 30–40%, 20–30%, 10–20%, less than 10%.

Question 3.4

The porosity will vary with grain size in the following ways:

(a)   For unconsolidated sediments, the larger the grain size, the lower the porosity (Table 3.1).

(b)   For consolidated shale and sandstone sediments, the larger the grain size, the higher the porosity.

Question 3.5

(a)   specific yield = porosity − specific retention

   $= (37 - 7)\% = 30\%$

(b)   Essentially, 'free' water was removed from an area of $8 \times 10^5 \, m^2$ of water-saturated rock to a depth of 5 m; a volume of $8 \times 10^5 \times 5 \, m^3$. Therefore, using Equation 3.5:

   volume removed (the exploitable storage)

   $= (8 \times 10^5 \times 5 \times 30/100) \, m^3$

   $= 1.2 \times 10^6 \, m^3$

(c)   Figure 3.16 suggests that the aquifer consists of fine gravels.

Question 4.1

(a)   The general shape of the hydrograph indicates a temperate maritime regime, with some contribution from melting snow in April. (The river is a British one, the Severn at Bewdley.)

(b)   The maximum discharge is about $310 \, m^3 \, s^{-1}$. This is almost five times greater than the mean of $62.5 \, m^3 \, s^{-1}$.

(c)   The high rates of discharge are caused by periods of heavy rain due to the passage of weather fronts.

Question 4.2

The baseflow contribution on the hydrograph is the consistent flow that is independent of the rainstorm peaks. Both mean baseflow and discharge over a period of months can only be estimated approximately.

(a)   Mean baseflow is about $80 \, m^3 \, s^{-1}$ over the November to April period, and mean discharge during this period is about $120 \, m^3 \, s^{-1}$, so baseflow is about 60% of discharge for the winter months.

(b)   Mean baseflow is about $15 \, m^3 \, s^{-1}$ over the May to October period, and mean discharge during this period is about $20 \, m^3 \, s^{-1}$, so baseflow is about 75% of discharge

for the summer months (when there is little evidence of overland flow, so the proportion contributed by the baseflow is relatively higher).

Question 5.1

(a)   The sudden decrease in oxygen a short distance downstream from the sewage outfall is caused by the oxidation of organic material, as shown by the increase in oxygen demand (BOD) just below the sewage outfall. After this, the water is slowly reoxygenated from the atmosphere and from aquatic plants, as the algal population increases.

(b)   Ammonia (NH_3) concentrations increase after sewage enters the river, then gradually decrease downstream. (The increase is due to nitrogen-containing compounds being decomposed by anaerobic bacteria. The values decrease downstream as the ammoniacal compounds are oxidized, giving an increase in nitrate (NO_3) concentrations.)

(c)   Bacteria, protozoa and sewage fungus appear to be most able to tolerate the pollution. These organisms are most abundant in the polluted parts of the river.

(d)   Organisms that tolerate low levels of dissolved oxygen are able to breed and thrive in the parts of the river closest to the sewage outfall. They have little competition and few predators. As the level of dissolved oxygen increases downstream, the less tolerant species are able to exist and may compete with others also able to survive there. As higher levels of dissolved oxygen are restored (that is, the river is self-purified), a more balanced aquatic ecosystem becomes established.

Question 5.2

Your answer to this will obviously depend on where you live. Near the OU in Milton Keynes the class of rivers is generally B, good. This compares well with the national average; 65% of English rivers fall into classes A, B and C in Table 5.2.

Question 5.3

(a)   The EU standards in Table 5.4 (Section 5.4) suggest that the water is suitable for a public water supply as far as indicated for the substances listed in Table 5.4 (but this is not the full list). However, the water may have to be treated to reduce any organic pollutants (not given in Table 5.5).

(b)   The water is unsuitable for irrigation as the sodium concentration is much greater than the combined calcium and magnesium concentrations.

Question 6.1

(a)   Santa Barbara — capital cost US\$36 million, output 12×10^6 m^3 a year. Over 10 years, capital cost repayment = US\$$3.6 \times 10^6$ per year, which is US\$3.6/12 per m^3 = US\$0.3 per m^3. At US\$1 = £0.55, this is £0.17 per m^3.

(b)   Isles of Scilly — capital cost £250 000, output 220 m^3 per day. This plant is for seasonal demand, so it may work for about 200 days a year. Therefore:

output per year = 220×200 m^3 = 4.4×10^4 m^3

capital cost repayment is £25 000 per year
= £25 000/4.4×10^4 per m^3

= £0.6 per m^3

The Isles of Scilly plant has a capital cost contribution per cubic metre about three or four times that of the Santa Barbara plant. This is probably due to the economies of scale for the Santa Barbara plant.

Question 7.1

The total amount of water abstracted in 2001 (Table 7.1) was:

43.11×10^6 m^3 per day

Quantity per person per day = $(43.11 \times 10^6 / 50 \times 10^6)$ m^3

= 0.86 m^3 or 860 litres

Question 7.2

(a)   Wales abstracts the greatest total quantity of water. A lot of this is transferred to other regions.

(b)   Thames abstracts the greatest amount of water for public water supply.

(c)   The Anglian, Southern and South West regions extract the greatest proportion of groundwater for public supply, and Wales the least.

COMMENTS ON ACTIVITIES

Activity 5.1

(a) I had two different types of bottled water at home: 'Buxton Carbonated Natural Mineral Water' and 'Mountain Spring Natural Mineral Water, Perthshire'.

	Concentration of dissolved substances/mg l^{-1}	
	Buxton	**Perthshire**
aluminium	0	
bicarbonate	248	128
calcium	55	27
chloride	42	9
iron	0	
magnesium	519	9
nitrate	less than 0.1	1
potassium	1	0.6
sodium	24	6
sulphate	23	6
TDS	280	128
pH	7.4	

(b) Neither of the bottles breaches the EU guidelines for the substances listed in Table 5.4.

Activity 5.2

There is obviously no single answer to this question! It will vary depending on where you live. Below I have given the answers for my house (which is in a small village to the south of Milton Keynes) so you can see the type of answer that could be given.

(a) Yes, my house has a piped water supply (and life would be very difficult without it).

(b) I had to telephone my local water company to check on this: although I thought I knew the answer it proved to be more complicated than I expected. I live on a good sandstone aquifer (the Cretaceous Lower Greensand) and expected my water supply to be just groundwater from local boreholes. However, although part of the supply comes from two local boreholes, this water is linked in a water grid to other parts of my water company region, so my local borehole water is blended with that from two major lowland reservoirs, Rutland Water and Grafham Water, 100 km and 60 km away. I presume this is for security of supply and quality purposes.

(c) Again, I had to ask the water company. The borehole water is just filtered and disinfected, but the reservoir water is screened, stored, settled, filtered and disinfected.

(d) In England and Wales you can get this information from your water company on request. I was sent an analysis for my water supply which showed it to be within the EU limits (Table 5.4, Section 5.4) except for iron, which had a mean concentration of 0.1 mg l^{-1} and a maximum of 0.42 mg l^{-1}, whereas the EU recommended maximum is 0.2 mg l^{-1}.

The water analysis was for a total of 101 different parameters (many more than in Table 5.4) and I was also sent the full prescribed concentration list from which I was able to work out that my supply breached regulations additionally for manganese, nitrite, pesticides and phosphorus.

The water company included details of the non-compliant concentrations under two headings: *Relaxations*, which have been granted by the Secretary of State to 'relax' the standards for naturally occurring substances (the iron and manganese); and *Undertakings*, where the water supply has become non-compliant due to human causes. Both relaxations and undertakings commit the water company to remedial action.

I found the high iron concentration unsurprising, as the sandstone aquifer supplying most of my water has a high concentration of iron. The high nitrite, phosphorus and pesticide values are in the reservoir water, and could be caused by agricultural runoff.

(e) I had a water meter installed in 1992, having calculated that it would save money on water bills to my house, and in the hope that it would also provide encouragement for me to use less water (it has).

(f) For 2003 I used a metered 64 m^3 of water at £1.13 per m^3, which cost £1.13 × 64 = £72.32.

> This is for two people, so cost per person = £36.16.

(g) My house is connected to a sewer.

(h, i) I knew the answer to part of this — that my village has its own small sewage works for primary and secondary treatment — but not the full story. My water company told me that the effluent is discharged to our local small river (the Ouzel) but the sludge is tankered 10 km to the major sewage works in Milton Keynes for further treatment: anaerobic digestion. The digested sludge is then spread on farmland.

(j)   The cost is £1.86 per m³, taken as 90% of the water supplied (as sewerage is not metered). So

total sewerage cost = £1.86 × 0.9 × 64 = £107.14

cost per person = £53.52

Activity 7.1

These are my results for the first week in June; yours will be different, but these might be useful to demonstrate how to go about this Activity.

Number of baths in a week = 1

Number of showers in a week = 5

Time taken by bath tap to fill a 1 litre jug = 3 s

Length of time tap runs to fill a bath = 3 minutes, 10 s = 190 s

Water used per bath = 190/3 litres = 61 litres

Time taken by shower to fill a 1 litre jug = 9 s

Water used per minute of shower = 60/9 litres = 7 litres

Total length of time for five showers = 37 minutes

Total water use for five showers = 7 × 37 litres = 259 litres

Total bath/shower water use per week = 61 + 259 litres = 320 litres

Averaged bath/shower water use per day = 320/7 litres = 46 litres

This is 46 litres/150 litres × 100% of the average daily use = 31%; coincidentally about the same as in Figure 1.2.

ACKNOWLEDGEMENTS

Among the many people who helped in various ways during the preparation of this book, the author would particularly like to thank Michael Price (ex-University of Reading) for specialist advice, and colleagues on the S278 Course Team (and on its predecessor, S268 *Physical Resources and Environment*) for their constructive suggestions.

Grateful acknowledgement is made to the following sources for permission to reproduce material within this product.

Figures 1.1, 4.4 and 4.6 Dr Andy Sutton, The Open University; *Figure 1.2* Crown copyright material is reproduced under Class Licence Number C01W0000065 with the permission of the Controller of HMSO and the Queen's Printer for Scotland; *Figures 1.3, 2.14, 4.2 and 6.9* Dr Sandy Smith, The Open University; *Figure 2.1* NASA; *Figure 2.3* Copyright © T. C. Middleton/Oxford Scientific Film; *Figure 2.5* ICRISAT Climate of Niamey, Progress Report No. 1, ICRISAT, Sahelian Centre, Niamey; *Figure 2.6* Copyright © Research Machines plc 2003; *Figure 2.9* Adapted from http://www.met-office.gov.uk/climate/uk/averages/images/RainAnnual6190.gif © Crown copyright, Met Office. Reproduced under licence number Met0/IPR/2; *Figure 2.12* Brandon, T. W. (ed.) (1986) *Groundwater: Occurrence, Development and Protection*, The Institute of Water and Environmental Management; *Figure 2.13 Water Resources: Planning for the Future*, Anglian Water Authority; *Figure 3.1* Copyright © British Geological Survey; *Figure 3.2* Dr Peter Sheldon, The Open University; *Figures 3.5 and 3.8* IWEM (1961) *Manual of British Water Engineering Practice*, The Institute of Water and Environmental Management; *Figures 3.11, 3.13 and 3.14* Cargo, D. N. and Mallory, R. F. (1974) *Man and His Geologic Environment*, Addison-Wesley Publishing Company; *Figure 3.12* Ward, R. C. (1975) *Principles of Hydrology*, 2nd edn, McGraw-Hill Book Company (UK) Limited. Copyright © 1967, 1975 McGraw-Hill Publishing Company Limited; *Figure 3.15* Geoscience Features Picture Library; *Figures 3.19 and 5.7* Sinclair Stammers/Science Photo Library; *Figure 3.21* CIRIA (1989) CIRIA Special Publication 69, Construction Industry Research and Information Association; *Figure 3.22* CEH Wallingford, Crowmarsh Gifford, Wallingford, Oxfordshire; *Figure 4.1* Copyright © Jos Joslin, National Trails Office; *Figure 4.10* National Rivers Authority; *Figure 4.11* Chorley, R. J., Schumm, S.A. and Sugden, D.E. (1984) *Geomorphology*, Methuen & Co; *Figure 4.12* Graf, W. L. (1985) *The Colorado River*, Resource Publications in Geography, Association of American Geographers, Washington, DC; *Figure 4.13* Bernhard Edmaier/Science Photo Library; *Figure 4.14* Copyright © Popperfoto; *Figure 4.17* photo by Winter and Kidson, courtesy Fairclough Civil Engineering Ltd; *Figure 4.21* © Reuters/Corbis; *Figure 5.1* Arthur Trees/Science Photo Library; *Figure 5.4* Roman Baths, Bath and NE Somerset Council; *Figure 5.5* Richard Hamilton-Smith/Corbis; *Figure 5.8* Copyright © Owen Mountford/Centre for Ecology and Hydrology; *Figure 5.9* Dr Peter Webb, The Open University; *Figure 5.10* Crown copyright material is reproduced under Class Licence Number C01W0000065 with the permission of the Controller of HMSO and the Queen's Printer for Scotland; *Figure 5.11* Copyright © Environment Agency; *Figure 5.12* Sir Frederick Warner (1994) Conference Paper No. 4,

Industry and Society, HRH The Duke of Edinburgh's Study Conference, July 1994; *Figure 5.14* David Riecks, Illinois–Indiana Sea Grant: courtesy Visualizing the Great Lakes: www.epa.gov/ginpo/image/; *Figure 5.15* Race Engineering, North Wales; *Figure 5.16* Environmental Consulting Associates, USA; *Figure 5.17* Peter Leeds-Harrison, Cranfield University; *Figure 5.18* Davie, T. (2002) *Fundamentals of Hydrology*, Routledge; *Figure 5.19* Courtesy of the Environment Agency; *Figure 5.20* Crown copyright material is reproduced under Class Licence Number C01W0000065 with the permission of the Controller of HMSO and the Queen's Printer for Scotland; *Figure 6.1* Dr Stuart Bennett, The Open University; *Figure 6.3* Recreatieschap Vinkeveense Plassen; *Figure 6.6* National Rivers Authority; *Figure 6.7* SPG Media Ltd; *Figure 6.8* © Tom Swafford, Desert Research Institute; *Figure 6.10* FreeFoto.com Ltd; *Figure 7.1* Southern Rural Water, Australia; *Figure 7.2* Taken from www.defra.gov.uk/ environment/statistics/inlwater/kf/iwkf12.htm Crown copyright material is reproduced under Class Licence Number C01W0000065 with the permission of the Controller of HMSO and the Queen's Printer for Scotland; *Figure 7.3* Walter Hunt, The Open University; *Figure 7.4* Aidan O'Rourke; *Figure 7.5* Taken from Met Office website. Crown copyright material is reproduced under Class Licence Number C01W0000065 with the permission of the Controller of HMSO and the Queen's Printer for Scotland; *Figure 7.6* Centre for Ecology and Hydrology, Wallingford (data source Climatic Research Unit/Hadley Centre); *Figures 7.7 and 7.8* Copyright © 2001 NERC's Centre for Ecology and Hydrology; *Figure 7.9* Dr Mike Dodd, The Open University; *Figure 7.10* Reproduced from the Ordnance Survey 1:3000000 map with the permission of Ordnance Survey on behalf of The Controller of Her Majesty's Stationery Office. © Crown copyright, licence number ED 100020607; *Figures 7.11 and 7.12* The Environment Agency 2004; *Figure 8.3* NASA; *Figure 8.4* Allan, J. A. (2002) *The Middle East Water Question: Hydropolitics and the Global Economy*, I. B. Tauris & Co. Ltd.

GLOSSARY

Items in this Glossary are printed in **bold** in the main text, usually where they are first mentioned. Terms printed in *italics* below are defined elsewhere in the Glossary.

apron   A horizontal impermeable layer at the foot of a dam to reduce downward seepage from a reservoir.

aquifer   A layer of rock that is sufficiently porous to store water, and permeable enough to allow water to flow through it. Aquifers can be *unconfined* (they crop out at the ground surface) or *confined* (separated from the ground surface by an impermeable layer). Contrast with *perched aquifer*.

aquifer storage and recovery (ASR)   A type of *managed aquifer recharge* that uses the same borehole to inject and recover *groundwater*.

artesian well   A well into a *confined aquifer*.

baseflow   The part of a river's *discharge* that has been derived directly from *groundwater*.

biochemical oxygen demand (BOD)   A measure of how much natural organic material is present in a body of water. It is defined as the amount of oxygen (in milligrams) taken up by micro-organisms in decomposing the organic material in a 1 litre sample stored in darkness for 5 days at 20 °C.

biodegradable   Referring to substances that can be broken down by bacteria and other organisms into relatively harmless end-products.

capillary retention   The process by which water (or any other liquid) tends to cling to the walls of narrow openings and move upwards through interconnected spaces.

catchment   The total land area drained by a river system, including all its tributaries.

cofferdam   A small temporary dam built to exclude water from a dam site while the dam is being built.

coliform count   The number of coliform bacteria present in a fixed volume of water. It is an indicator of faecal pollution.

cone of depression   The area where the *water table* or *potentiometric surface* is reduced around a pumped well.

confined aquifer   See *aquifer*.

conjunctive use   The combined use of surface water and *groundwater*, in a unified way, to optimize resource use and minimize the adverse effects of using a single source.

consumptive use   A use of water in which it is temporarily lost as a resource.

cutoff curtain   A narrow vertical impermeable structure extending below a dam to reduce the horizontal seepage of water under the dam.

Darcy's law   Relates the volume of *groundwater* flowing in unit time (*Q*) to the *hydraulic conductivity K* and the *hydraulic gradient h/l* by the equation:

$$Q = KAh/l$$

desalination   The production of fresh water from *saline water* (often seawater) by removal or reduction in concentration of the dissolved minerals in it.

direct supply reservoir   A reservoir to store water for steady release by pipeline to the public supply distribution system.

discharge   The volume of water (as in a river) that flows past a point in a certain time.

discharge consent   An agreement on the total volume, *BOD* and suspended solid concentration of an *effluent* than can be discharged to a stream or river in the UK. There is no fixed standard, as it depends on the character and use of the river.

discharge hydrograph   A graph of river *discharge* with time. Usually abbreviated to *hydrograph*.

drawdown   The difference in height between the *water table* or *potentiometric surface* in a well before and during pumping.

drought   A period when there is insufficient rainfall to maintain adequate water levels in rivers, reservoirs and *aquifers*.

effluent   The relatively clear liquid product of sewage or industrial waste treatment. This is mainly water.

evaporation   The process by which water is transferred as vapour from the land or ocean to the atmosphere.

evapotranspiration   The combined effects of *evaporation* and *transpiration*.

exploitable storage   The volume of water an *aquifer* will yield.

gravity dam   A dam that uses its own weight to prevent deformation or movement in order to withstand the pressure of water in a reservoir.

groundwater   Underground water in the *saturated zone*, below the *water table*.

hardness   Hardness in water is caused by the presence of calcium, iron and magnesium ions: the higher the concentration of these ions, the harder the water. Hard water is difficult to lather, needing more soap, and leaves scale on appliances.

head   The difference in height of a *water table* at two locations.

humidity   A measure of how close air is to saturation with water vapour.

hydraulic conductivity   A measure of the volume of water that will flow through a unit cross-sectional area of rock per unit time, under a unit *hydraulic gradient* and at a specified temperature: K in the *Darcy's law* equation.

hydraulic gradient   The slope of a *water table*.

hydrograph   An abbreviation of *discharge hydrograph*.

hydrological cycle   Another name for the *water cycle*.

hydrologically effective precipitation   The quantity of water available from underground or from rivers in an area, given by the excess of *precipitation* over actual *evapotranspiration*.

hydrology   The study of water movement on and beneath the ground, and the physics and chemistry of water.

hydrosphere   The parts of the Earth that are mainly composed of water.

infiltration   The movement of water through the ground surface into soil or rock and on downwards towards the *water table*.

interception   The process by which plants stop *precipitation* reaching the ground.

interception loss   The proportion of *precipitation* that does not reach the ground as a result of *interception*.

interflow   Underground water moving through the *unsaturated zone*, that is, above the *water table*.

irrigation   The managed watering of crops so they can be grown in areas where they could otherwise not be grown, or to improve the yield.

leachate   A solution that forms as water percolates through landfill waste.

managed aquifer recharge   A type of *conjunctive use* in which excess surface water is stored underground in an *aquifer*.

meteoric water   Fresh water derived by condensation from the atmosphere and which accumulates as surface water or underground water.

mineral water   Saline *groundwater* discharged at the ground surface.

net gain   The amount by which natural river flow is augmented by pumping in a *river augmentation* scheme, usually expressed as a percentage of the pumped quantity.

non-consumptive use   A use of water which does not involve major diversions from its natural path and does not change its quality.

oasis   A natural artesian spring in a desert.

overland flow   Water that flows across the ground surface, excluding that in streams and rivers.

pathogenic bacteria   Bacteria that can cause disease in humans.

perched aquifer   An *aquifer* above the main *water table*, caused by a local, thin, impermeable layer.

permeability   A measure of the properties of a rock which determine how easily water (or any other fluid) can move through it.

plant nutrients   Inorganic substances, mainly nitrogen and phosphorus, that are essential for normal plant growth.

pollution   A harmful effect on the environment caused by human activity. Water pollution is a change in the quality of water due to human activity that makes the water less suitable for use than it was originally.

pores   Spaces within a rock.

porosity   The proportion of the rock volume that consists of *pores*.

potential evapotranspiration   The maximum *evapotranspiration* that could take place given an unlimited supply of moisture.

potentiometric surface   An imaginary surface joining the positions to which water will rise in a well, or above the ground surface. For an *unconfined aquifer* this is the *water table*.

precipitation   The process involved or the water that is transferred in solid or liquid form from the atmosphere to the Earth's surface.

pumped storage reservoir   A reservoir that does not fill naturally, but needs water to be pumped into it.

rain-making   Attempting to induce an increase in *precipitation* by artificial means. Sometimes referred to as 'cloud seeding'.

rating curve   A plot of *discharge* values of a river measured at various *stages*, with a smooth curve drawn through the plotted points.

recharge area   The area where an *aquifer* outcrops.

reservoir   When used in connection with the *water cycle*, this is a part of the *hydrosphere* that stores water temporarily. Also a means of artificial water storage.

residence time   The average time that water stays in a *reservoir* before moving to another reservoir; e.g. the average time that a water molecule spends in the atmosphere before falling to the ground as rain or snow.

river augmentation   A scheme of *conjunctive use* that uses *groundwater* to increase the flow of a river when the *discharge* is low. The river is used to convey the groundwater to where it is needed without the need to build a pipeline.

river regulation   The release of stored water from reservoirs into a river when the natural *discharge* is low, so that it can be abstracted for use further downstream.

safe yield   The maximum quantity of water that can be removed from an *aquifer* each year without adverse effects.

saline intrusion   A wedge of seawater under fresh *groundwater* near a coastline, caused by excessive groundwater extraction.

saline water   Surface water with a high *TDS*; this is seawater in the oceans and some lakes.

salinization   The accumulation of salts in the soil that may occur with irrigated agriculture.

saturated zone   A zone below the *unsaturated zone*, where all the *pores* are filled with water. This is *groundwater*.

sludge   The nasty-smelling, thick liquid product of sewage treatment.

specific discharge   The volume of *groundwater* flowing through a unit cross-sectional area.

specific retention   The proportion of the water in an *aquifer* that is retained around the individual grains by surface tension, and cannot be extracted.

specific yield   The proportion of the water that can be recovered from an *aquifer*.

stage   The water level in a river.

sustainable development   Development that meets the needs of the present without compromising the ability of future generations to meet their own needs. A sustainable resource can be supplied indefinitely, without causing irreversible damage to the environment.

total dissolved solids (TDS)   The concentration of dissolved solid substances in water.

transpiration   The process by which plants draw water from the soil and transfer it to their leaves, from which it evaporates through pores in the leaf system.

unconfined aquifer   See *aquifer.*

unsaturated zone   A zone just below the ground surface, where *pores* are mainly filled with air. See *saturated zone*.

virtual water   The water used to produce the goods that a country imports.

wall dam   A rigid dam that withstands the pressure of water in a reservoir by transferring the pressure to the floor and sides of a valley.

water cycle   The natural cycle by which water is circulated between the Earth's surface (on or under it) and the atmosphere. In essence, water is evaporated from the oceans, forms clouds, is precipitated on land as rain, hail or snow, and then flows in rivers, glaciers or underground to the sea, where it is evaporated again.

water table   The level of water in a well (strictly in a well that just penetrates the *water table*). It is also the boundary surface between the *unsaturated zone* and *saturated zone*.

water transfer   The transfer of water from one river *catchment* to another. It can increase the supply of water in an area by transferring it from areas with surplus water. Part of Birmingham's water, for example, comes from Wales.

INDEX

Note that **bold** page numbers refer to where terms defined in the Glossary are printed in **bold** in the text.